Marlene
685 Mcparland Rd #202
Madison, Wisconsin
53713

Memoirs:
Half a Century
In Nursing

STELLA GOOSTRAY

1886 - 1969

Memoirs:

Half a Century

In Nursing

by
Stella Goostray

NURSING ARCHIVE
BOSTON UNIVERSITY MUGAR MEMORIAL LIBRARY
BOSTON   MASSACHUSETTS

THE NURSE'S BOOK SOCIETY EDITION

Foreword

When Stella Goostray, during her last illness, embarked upon the writing of these Memoirs it was not her intent to prepare them for publication but rather to record experiences which she knew to have significance for the nursing profession. Her interest in nursing history made her aware of the dearth of first hand accounts by nurses. The document was to be placed in the Nursing Archive at Mugar Library at Boston University, a historical collection in which she took interest and to which she had contributed her personal papers in the knowledge they would be accessible to future students in nursing. Eventually she was prevailed upon to permit private publication of the book and generous friends have made this possible.

Associates and friends of Stella Goostray would attest to the personal qualities which they admired and which made possible her contribution to her profession. A fine mind which she used in an exceptionally logical, ordered and objective way, energy which she expended freely for sound purposes, singular freedom from petty personal judgments and personal competitiveness, a keen sense of humor and a great capacity for friendship were some of her characteristics. These qualities and her commitment to the improvement of nursing combined to make her one of a small band of notable nurses who extended enormous influence in nursing affairs in her time.

The Memoirs, perhaps in part because of their informality, reflect her personality so that those who knew her well will feel her presence. Others who did not have that privilege will find them valuable and interesting because they record, from her central vantage point and in a lively fashion, some aspects of events which may not appear in more formal histories.

The history of the period is recorded elsewhere; these Memoirs bring alive the times as experienced by one who was there. And they were crucial and exciting times. The thirties, years of much misery and social unrest, saw stirrings in nursing education which laid the groundwork for later developments. The war slowed some of the hoped for progress but thereafter momentum was reestablished and despite the fact that some directions may have changed, the work of nursing leaders in the thirties provided a foundation for a new era.

During World War II, Miss Goostray was one of a small number of nurses who bore enormous responsibility to chart for the profession a course which would serve the needs of the country and at the same time avoid disastrous steps backward in nursing and nursing education. A taxing and at times a disheartening assignment for those involved.

Some of the pride she felt in nursing is apparent in these writings: notably the contribution during the war years and the profession's fight for equal recognition of Negro nurses. Today one surely will read with incredulity the difficulties the members of the National Nursing Council for War Service encountered in their efforts to achieve equal status for these nurses in the Armed Forces of the United States.

Perhaps we have come farther in a generation than we yet know; the country, toward the goal of freedom and justice; the nursing profession, toward a full realization of the contribution which it can make to a better society. Stella Goostray believed nursing could and should be an instrument for that purpose and she helped to make it possible.

Muriel B. Vesey
Director, School of Nursing
and Nursing Service
The Children's Hospital
Medical Center, Boston

Introduction

FROM time to time, some of my friends in nursing have suggested that I put into writing some of the things I have told them about other days in nursing. Occasionally I did jot down a note and put it in a folder. When on my 80th birthday, a card arrived from Edith Patton Lewis (sometime editor of the *American Journal of Nursing,* a fellow member of the National Committee on Historical Source Materials in Nursing, and now a sort of "roving editor" of the Journal, since she goes where the news is) with the comment, "still think you should get to work on your memoirs," I decided that it was time to begin, if they were ever to be written. I was entering that decade of which a modern translator of the Psalms, Ronald Knox, described as "for the most part weakness, toil and frustration." But not until the last six months did I make much headway. This prelude is being written in October 1968.

When I told a friend in the spring of 1964 that I was about to take off on a trip around the world, he shouted over the telephone, "Stella, are you off your rocker?" I assured him that I had never been in it. And one of the reasons for jotting down the notes was that if the memoirs ever were written they might serve to interest me when I had to sit and rock.

These memoirs relate to my personal career in nursing as well as to my association with the broader field of nursing education. The collected notes were the source of materials used for the preparation of two unpublished papers. One was "There Were Other Changing Times," read at the Annual Convention of the Massachusetts League for nursing, November 18, 1966; the second "Challenge and Change" at the meeting under the aegis of the Committee on Historical Source Materials in Nursing at the National League for Nursing Convention,

May 11, 1967. Now in turn these papers are amplified for these memoirs. Use has also been made of a third paper, read at a meeting of the New Jersey State Nurses' Association in 1935, published in the *American Journal of Nursing,* August 1935, and also as a reprint: "What Lies Ahead for the Nursing Profession."

One who writes memoirs and publishes them puts himself into the orchestra of those who like to "toot their own tuppenny horns" so I hasten to add here that these memoirs were not intended for general publication. Neither do they make any pretense of being an in-depth analysis or history of the historical events with which some of them are concerned; therefore I am not bound by certain limitations imposed on historians. It was my privilege to have been associated with some of the important movements in nursing in the days when I believe the profession began "to grow up." I shall try to tell what we did to develop that maturity and to tell it "as it was." Some of the behind the scenes encounters were not always pleasant while they lasted but I see no reason for trying to bury them in the sands of obscurity. They do indicate some of the rocky road that had to be traveled to bring the profession where it is today. It is my hope that in the personal memoirs, as well as the general reminiscences, a reader may penetrate what at first reading may seem "trivia" and find indications of the status of nursing at that time.

Memory is not always reliable so that an effort has been made to document some of the material. I did have the opportunity two years ago to look over some of the minutes of the National League of Nursing Education, for the period I was on the Board as secretary and later as president, and to have copies made of some minutes showing important actions taken by the Board. When I retired I destroyed my personal copies of the minutes of the NLNE as well as those of the National Nursing Council for War Service. Unfortunately the official minutes of the latter were destroyed at national headquarters. The stenographic reports of the meetings of the Committee on the Grading of Nursing Schools are in the Goostray Collection, Nursing Archive, Mugar Library, Boston University, Boston, and cover the period 1930-1934. They may well be the only ones in existence. How they escaped my destructive hand in 1946 I shall never know. Since those destructive days I have learned better and do penance by urging my young colleagues in nursing to hunt for and save historical materials.

Accompanying the manuscript of these memoirs in the Nursing Archive, Mugar Library, is a file containing documentary evidence for many references. Sources for other references are in the Goostray Collection and are so indicated. The books referred to are available in most school of nursing libraries. Following the reference materials are newspaper clippings and memorabilia which have relevance to events covered by the memoirs. At least the newspaper pictures will show the fashions of the day. Most of the newspaper clippings I found among my father's belongings. When I was away from home at conventions I used to send him the newspaper accounts, especially if there were any items concerning his younger daughter's activities. After his death I found the clippings, carefully preserved.

These memoirs never would have been completed without the help of members of my family who made editorial suggestions and Children's Hospital friends who brought NLNE League reports to me and checked references of which I was not too sure. Especially am I indebted to Mary Ann Garrigan, curator, Nursing Archive, Mugar Library, who not only gave encouragement but furnished a tape recorder and had the tapes transcribed.

So here go the memoirs for what they are worth.

Stella Goostray

February 21, 1969

Contents

Memoirs:
Half a Century
In Nursing

Chapter One

A STUDENT NURSE
IN THE CHILDREN'S HOSPITAL

THE thought of entering a School of Nursing had been in my mind at various times partly because I knew a number of Children's Hospital graduates and also the Sisters who were in charge there. However, my decision was triggered in 1915 when I had to make a decision about going to Philadelphia to live because the national headquarters of a religious organization of the Episcopal Church, of which I was assistant to the editor of its magazine, were being transferred from Boston to Philadelphia. World War I had begun in Europe, one of my friends was with the Harvard Unit of the British Expeditionary Forces and, of course, the talk was that "we" would soon be in it. I then made my decision to enter a school and hoped that if the United States entered the war I might serve abroad. I did go to Philadelphia for several months but not before making application to enter the Children's Hospital School of Nursing. I well remember plodding up the long flight of stone steps in front of the Children's Hospital. These steps were torn down in 1968.

The person who interviewed me was Helen Wood, whose name is now well known as a leading nurse educator in the 'twenties and 'thirties when I knew her in various capacities, and especially when she was a member of the Committee on the Grading of Nursing Schools of which I was a consultant. Later she was the Director of the School at Simmons College, and I was Director of the Children's Hospital School. We had a joint five-year program leading to a Bachelor of Science degree so that we had many relationships. New England to the backbone, forthright, with common sense and good judgment, Helen Wood could always be relied upon in matter of nursing education. We became good friends. But I am getting ahead of my story.

On December 8, 1915, I arrived at the Children's Hospital, Boston, with three pink striped probationers' uniforms long enough when worn to come within four inches of the ground, a dozen gathered aprons with two buttonholes in which pearl studs were worn, black stockings, orthopedic shoes, half-a-dozen pairs of stiff cuffs and a dozen "Buster Brown" collars, $300 to pay my tuition, and extra money for books.

At that time students were taken into the school several times a year and Mary Norcross, whom I had known slightly for several years, had entered in September. Most of the group in the December section were girls from eighteen to twenty years old, but one, Georgia Hukill from Franklin, Pennsylvania, was a month older than I and both of us had passed our twenty-ninth birthday. Needless to say she, Mary Norcross and I became close friends and still are. Helen Wood was no longer there, she having been at the Children's only a year as an interim person. The Sisters of St. Margaret had hoped to put in a Sister Superintendent of Nurses again. This, however, did not take place.

The new principal of the school was Elizabeth E. Sullivan, a Massachusetts General graduate and one of the best teachers I have ever had. She not only administered the school and the nursing service, but taught us the principles and practice of nursing.

Our group and the group which had entered in September began our semester at Simmons College early in February and I lasted one day! At the end of that day when I got back to the nurses' residence, the Sister-in-Charge took one look at me and said, "Are you sick?" The answer was "Yes." I had fainted at prayers the morning before. My temperature was taken and it was 104°. I had typhoid fever and what a stir in the hospital! Probationers, as we were called, were not supposed to be assigned to patients with infectious diseases since we had as yet no instruction in medical asepsis, nor did we have immunization for typhoid fever.

Several weeks before I was on duty on the lower ward of the medical unit but was sent upstairs because they seemed to have an emergency. One half of the upstairs unit had only children with typhoid fever, and probationers were not assigned there.

The emergency was created by a senior student who had left the water running in the typhoid hopper. The typhoid stools were there and they had not been sterilized by steam. The hopper room and the hallway were flooded. The student head nurse told me to clean up the mess. No wonder I got typhoid fever. Thereafter all students were given typhoid vaccine.

What I remember most about that illness is my stay at the Peter Bent Brigham Hospital and the slush baths I was given. The patient was laid in a rubber sheet with the sides turned up to make a trough while the nurse poured ice water over her. It was harsh treatment I can tell you. The resident on the service was Dr. Samuel Levine, later to become the famous specialist. I liked him, for if a nurse were not available, he helped out. Then there was the kindly Dr. Francis Peabody, Chief of the Medical Staff. I had lots of kidding because I was a bad actor about eating and for days my diet was champagne. Day after day Sister Florence Hilda, House Mother at the Children's, came over and tried to spoon-feed semi-solid food into me, and even milk with a medicine dropper when I was seriously ill.

Two visitors from the Brigham Nursing Staff became my very good friends in later years, Carrie M. Hall, the Director of the School, and her assistant, Sally Johnson, later Director of the Massachusetts General Hospital School. Many a jigsaw puzzle Mary Hall (outside professional life she was Mary not Carrie) helped me with, and in after years many a one we did together in Blue Hill, Maine, where she used to visit us.

After a long convalesence and despite the protestation of family and friends, I re-entered the School in February 1917. I thought then that I had entered a good school of nursing and knew it for sure when

[3]

I saw the reports of the State Approved Schools which participated in the grading study about ten years after my graduation. Even though my view of nursing education has broadened considerably, I believe that I had an excellent education in terms of nursing education of that day, and I have never regretted my choice of school. But even then as a student I did wonder about some things. For example, I could not understand why we had at least two months and the September section five months on the hospital wards with classes in the principles and practice of nursing or practical nursing as it was dubbed, before or concurrently studying any of the underlying sciences.

The program at Simmons College was well planned for students in nursing. There were courses in chemistry, bacteriology, anatomy and physiology, sanitation, and nutrition and cooking. The courses in the sciences were excellent, but I thought that the course on nutrition and cooking was "for the birds." Four points of college credits were given for the main sciences but I do not remember what point value was given the courses in nutrition and cooking and sanitation. The instructors in anatomy and physiology and chemistry were men, and the course in sanitation was given by Professor Hilliard, who was well known in his field. Bacteriology was taught by a woman professor.

While we were at Simmons we worked on the wards every other weekend. We were given our "strawberry box" caps, as the children call them, when we had passed the examination in the principles and practice of nursing. At the end of the Simmons term we were given a narrow black velvet band for our cap and again at the beginning of the second and third years. When we became student head nurses we wore a wide black velvet band on one strap of our apron bib.

Social regulations were rather rigid. For example, it was against regulations to go out with a member of another class, so when I had to drop out and come back again, I was not supposed (note, I say "not supposed") to go out with my former friends. Of course, to be found going out with an intern was a serious offense, but you had better believe that these rules for many students were only on the books!

It will be remembered that I was older than the average student and therefore probably more critical of the time we spent doing jobs that had little relation to nursing, such as putting away the laundry and refolding sheets, etc., so that the linen closet was really a joy to look at. But the linen closet looked that way for only a few hours. The linen had to be used, and after baths in the morning empty shelves faced us. The folding of linen always seemed to me to be a great waste of energy, especially when there were so many other things to do that we often had to stay on after seven p.m. to get them done.

These were the days of "show beds." After a patient was discharged, and the bedframe washed and gone over with a weak solution of formalin, the mattress turned and a fresh mattress cover put on, the bed was made up. Instead of the top sheet and spread being turned over the blanket, they were brought even with the top of the mattress and a "sham sheet," which was about eighteen inches wide, was placed across the bed, and then the pillow. When a new patient arrived, the orderly and patient waited while the nurse removed the pillow and sham sheet and turned the spread and top sheet over the blanket and opened the bed, a procedure which took quite a few minutes.

When the maid was on her afternoon off and when a relief maid did not come, which was often, we had to wash the dishes before they went into the sterilizer, and to sweep the ward floor. Yet I am sure we had much less housekeeping to do than was required in most of the schools of that day.

Of course we were supposed to open the doors for doctors, and if they washed their hands a student nurse stood with an open towel ready to drop over their wet hands.

These were the days when the administrator of the hospital and the superintendent of nurses made an inspection tour together once a week, and well I remember those days both at the Children's and the Massachusetts General. That was the morning when cleaning took precedence over patient care, and I know at the Children's some of the student head nurses — for the head nurses were usually senior students — encouraged the night nurse to get as many baths given as she could.

I never expected in those days to be in that hospital as director of nursing and of the school. But I used to say to myself that if ever I came back in the capacity of a graduate nurse and had any influence over some of the regulations, one of the things that would be changed was the practice of getting children up to be weighed very early in the morning and giving some of them baths on inspection day when they should have been having their sleep. And those things were changed eventually.

One morning Sister Caroline, the administrator, came on the ward early without the superintendent of nurses. She found another student and me polishing the brass knobs on the black orthopedic beds. These beds were different from the others in the hospital and had been brought from the old building on Huntington Avenue. The sides of the bed were on a hinge arrangement so that they could be opened and fall below the mattress, giving an opportunity for the use of all kinds of orthopedic appliances. There were brass knobs on each of the four corners. Sister Caroline came over to us and said, "You are here to care for the children, not to polish brass. This is part of the maid's work." You can jolly well believe we did not do much polishing after that, nor did the head nurse ask us to.

When I became Director of Nursing, it did not take me too long to get the administrator to give up formal inspection tours on a regular day. But this does not mean that no inspecting was done. In fact, I did quite a lot, but at no scheduled time. One of the pass words when I first came as director was "Don't let Goostray catch you using a diaper to polish the sterilizer."

In these days of complicated equipment I look back at the simple equipment of our day. A frequent treatment was saline by Murphy drip. This was given by rectum, and the equipment consisted of a thermos bottle with a two hole rubber stopper. In one hole was inserted a glass tube which went nearly to the bottom of the bottle. A rubber connecting tube and a rectal tube were attached. The other hole had a small piece of glass tubing to allow for air pressure.

Cold air treatment was the order of the day for patients with pneumonia and also for the student nurse who had to go out on the porch to care for them. We always had to have sweaters nearby, whether we had a pneumonia patient or not. The wards were of the pavilion type, supposedly the latest thing in hospital construction. They had overhead ventilation and three large sliding doors to the open porch. The doors leaked like sieves even with sandbags against them.

One of the treatments given for nephritis was a steambath. A tent-shaped apparatus was set up in the bed, a length of pipe inserted from the bottom of the bed, and steam introduced into the pipe from a kettle on an electric plate at the bottom of the bed. Believe me, one was scared to death of a possible accident.

We always felt sorry for the children with diabetes whose main diet consisted of bacon, lettuce, cream and butter, and we always had to be on the watch if they were out of bed to prevent snitching from the little diet kitchen.

These were the days when empyema was a frequent sequela to pneumonia. In those days there were no antibiotics. A rib resection was done, and a rubber Murphy button was inserted through which the drainage could take place and the wound could be irrigated. When a child was admitted with a diagnosis of appendicitis, more often than not the appendix was ruptured. After operation, the application of flaxseed poultices was the usual treatment. When I had my experience at night on a surgical ward for older children, there was scarcely a night when there were not at least half a dozen children on the ward having flaxseed poultices. Years afterwards the night supervisor told me that she never saw me on her nightly visit when I was not making a flaxseed poultice. The morning salute from my fellow night dutiers at breakfast was "How many poultices last night, Goose?" I later calculated that I had made approximately 600 during the eight weeks of night duty.

In the orthopedic wards, many of the patients had bone tuberculosis, usually of the spine or hip — conditions infrequently found these days, thanks to the pasteurization of milk. After the poliomyelitis epidemic, especially the one in Vermont, many children came to the Children's Hospital for the correction of severe deformities. I can remember seeing children whose only means of locomotion was crawling on their knees and elbows. With their poor little twisted bodies they were a pathetic sight.

On the infants' surgical ward, the most frequent diagnoses were harelip and cleft palate, intussusception, and pyloric stenosis. It was an historic occasion in the Children's Hospital, when I was there in charge of the school and nursing service, and Dr. Donald W. Mac-Collum operated on one hundred infants with pyloric stenosis without a single fatality. An American flag was tied to the bed of the one-hundredth infant. Even though the operation was successful, that record would not have been possible without the skilled nursing care that was given.

Another thing that bothered me was that students were put into situations for which they had no preparation. How well I remember when I was put "on call" for the operating room after I had been there for a few days, and my previous duties had consisted of cleaning up after operations. I had never actually been in the operating room during an operation. Of course that night there was an emergency. Dr. Ladd, the Chief Surgeon, was operating on a seriously injured child who had been in an automobile accident the day before but was not thought by his parents to have been seriously injured. I shall never forget the popping sound when Dr. Ladd opened the abdomen and the blood gushed out, nor shall I ever forget the scorn in his voice when he asked for a suture. The supervisor who was supposed to be telling me what to do was out of the room. I handed him one and he shouted, "Look at the size of the needle she hands me." Years later we laughed together about that episode. Of course, he had not remembered, but I had. No wonder the doctors, under the stress of the situation and the kind of help they sometimes had, cursed and threw instruments, a frequent mode of behavior on the part of some. Dr. Ladd did neither, but the scorn in his voice was enough. He was a great surgeon, and my later associations with him when I was Director of Nursing are of the kind I like to remember. Only once did we have a few unpleasant words during the stress of war days, and afterwards he came to my office and apologized.

One thing we learned without doubt at the Children's Hospital was nicety in nursing procedures, and if there was sloppy work it was soon called to our attention by a supervisor or one of the staff. Dr. Robert Lovett, the eminent orthopedic surgeon, was especially particular about bandages. If he saw a leg in traction with an untidy looking bandage (and all bandages were turned in those days), he would say, "This isn't the alms house." This became a much used remark when something was not just snappy enough to suit us.

What we should be remembering about Dr. Robert Lovett was his strong plea for changes in nursing education. His address at the graduation exercise when the plan for the Simmons course was announced is a fine statement of the status of nursing education in the early 1900's. An extract of Dr. Lovett's address will be found in the School's history.

Children's Hospital students of my day always remember the red flannel jackets which the children wore over their johnnies. Each child had a new one on Christmas morning. And an event long remembered was circus day. In those days the circus grounds were on Huntington Avenue, so we had elephants and horses and not just a few selected entertainers.

It is surprising to me how many children I can remember by name after nearly fifty years. I would like to tell the story of a four-year-old boy who had a double harelip and whose teeth grew out like tusks. George had never been allowed to be with the rest of the members of his family, and when he came into the hospital he cowered every time anyone went near him. Eventually he was operated on and there was a beautiful result. The first day that he was allowed to be up, I dressed him in the nicest little suit I could find. And then I held a mirror in front of him so that he could look at himself. Never shall I forget the look of happiness on that child's face.

The head nurse wrote on her report when I was taking care of George that I had "pets." Of course I did, because they were children who I thought needed a little special attention. My classmates told me that I always picked out the "nit wits." I could have written a report on the head nurse which would have said, "She has 'pets' among the interns."

An Introduction to Social Service

In the summer of 1967, the hospital observed the fiftieth commemoration of the reorganization of the Social Service Department. Prior to 1917 there was a combined social service — visiting nurse service. I am quoting in part what I said on that occasion, because it brings in some of the reactions of the students to the new organization.

1917 was a year of changes, and these changes did not go unrecognized by the students. The Sisters withdrew from the hospital, and the students felt keenly the loss of the beloved Sister in charge of the students' residence. I don't think it made too much difference to them about the Sister Superintendent, for most of them only saw her when she came on the wards once a week with the Superintendent of Nurses to make the rigid inspection reminiscent of army inspections. As a matter of fact, discipline in a school of nursing of those days was of the military order. But as when old traditional ways are changed to meet new needs, there were resistence and resentment on the part of many students that district nursing and medical social service had been divorced. The change to the new order was not very happily accepted by the students who had looked forward to the combined services. And to add insult to injury some of the students didn't relish having a course of lectures on social problems added to the curriculum, because all too often in those war days classes had to come out of their two hours off duty.

I was one of the early students who had the three months' experience in social service . . . Someone once asked me how I happened to know many of the little streets in the South End and Roxbury. My reply was, 'Wearing out shoe-leather for the Social Service Departments of the Children's and of the Boston Dispensary, for

I spent one summer there. There were few automobiles around. There was a trolley car that ran from Park Street to Brookline Village via Longwood Avenue, but sometimes it was easier to walk to Roxbury or the South End — although I must say the girls today would have an easier time walking in their mini-skirts than we did.

The time in the Social Service Department was a very meaningful experience for me. Students shared in the staff conferences, and as we became familiar with the techniques of home visits, which I had under the tutelage of Miss Wilson by going on home visits with her, we were put 'on our own.'[1]

When I went back to the Children's as Director of the School, I got a great kick out of reading some of the reports on my work as a student. Miss Wilson wrote that she thought I was "a bit overconfident," but she did concede that my suggestions had shown that with practice I would "show excellent judgment in social treatment." Perhaps I was a little too sure of myself, but I take glory in the fact that I once saved the department from "pulling a boner."

I was assigned to a case in which the Social Service Department had planned to move a woman and her child from Cambridge to South Boston, and I was sent to South Boston to make the final arrangements about renting a flat for her. She needed and got assistance from the City of Cambridge, and it suddenly dawned on me that she would not be eligible for assistance from the City of Boston. So I did not make the arrangements but hied back to the hospital to pose the questions to Miss Wilson. I will not record her expression and remark, but the woman and child remained in Cambridge.

Although this is out of chronological order, I will continue with a few remarks about social service. During the summer following the first semester I was at Teachers College I worked at the Boston Dispensary in charge of the pediatric clinic. All of the workers in charge of clinics there were social workers, not nurses. It was a very enjoyable experience, because I met and joined in the conferences with people like Kate McMahon and Janet Thornton, both well-known in the field of social work, and Michael Davis, who was the Director of the Dispensary.

The next summer, Janet Thornton, who was about to go to New York to be in charge of the Social Service Department at the Presbyterian Hospital, asked me to go as her assistant. I thanked her and replied that I had already accepted a job as an instructor at the Philadelphia General Hospital. Her comment was, "What do you want to do that for? Anyone can teach nurses." That riled me. Unfortunately, the general attitude among social workers of the time was that student nurses were not of the same calibre intellectually as were student social workers. It is quite true, of course, that many student nurses did not have as broad an educational background, nor the freedom to initiate action and make decisions as did student social workers. Today social workers have much more respect for nursing education.

At the Massachusetts General Hospital

My affiliation at the Massachusetts General Hospital began on New Year's Day, 1919, and my first assignment was to a female medical ward filled to overflowing with influenza patients. I recall that there were a student head nurse, a "probationer," and myself on the ward that day. I like to remember that the "probationer" was Marjorie Stimson, who was later Professor of Public Health Nursing at Simmons College, and she likes to remind me that I bossed her around and told her that she "didn't pick up" after herself. I remember, too, that when I was assigned from a surgical ward to help wheel tonsillectomy patients back to the emergency ward (and literally dumped them in bed since they were too heavy for us to lift), on one occasion my partner for the job was Rachel Louise Metcalfe (McManus), later to become a well-known nurse educator. That was the only assignment I did not like. I told Miss Wood, then Acting Director (as Miss Parsons was overseas), to whom I had made application to enter the Children's

Hospital School of Nursing, that I thought such an assignment had little to do with my nursing education in medical or surgical nursing, and she agreed with me.

On some of the wards there was a blocked-up fireplace in the center of the ward, and the head nurse's desk was there. In some of the single rooms off the wards, usable fireplaces remained. On one ward in the middle of ward rounds, the chief was served a bowl of hot soup. I believe he had a medical condition which necessitated food in the middle of the morning! Inspection day was a big day, and, as in other hospitals, the nurses did little that morning but get ready for the fingers of the "inspectors" to be drawn across the rods of the beds or the windowsills.

We lived in Thayer Home, built in 1883, and there was heat only in the living room and the corridors, so each morning there was a race to get near the heat register in the centre of the corridor. We had bowls and pitchers in our rooms, and toothbrushes used the previous night were often frozen in the morning. Many times did I share the same register with Katherine Faville, whose later career included being Director of Henry Street Visiting Nurse Service, and Dean of Wayne University School of Nursing, as well as holding many important posts in national nursing affairs.

Miss Annabelle McCrae lived on the first floor. I believe her apartment was heated, at least I hope so. She was a formidable silencer of noises, and no one who ever saw her do it will forget when she came on the ward and found a bed which did not suit her standard of a well-made bed; she put her hands under one corner of the bedclothes and ripped it open. But withall she was a great teacher of the art of nursing.

Students assigned as temperature nurses on the ward went on duty at six a.m. and then went to breakfast after completing the job. There were no heated carts of food sent to the ward in those days. We hauled up food boxes on the dumb-waiter and at breakfast time were expected to boil the eggs in the ward kitchen. We did it by running hot water from the faucets over them. We toasted the bread, and if the patient wanted a second piece he or she had a long time to wait. The food was carried to the patients on heavy but lovely brass trays.

A person whom I knew once sent a squab for one of the semi-private patients in one of the rooms attached to the ward. I think she thought nurses had nothing else to do but cook for these people. Even at that time there were still persons in the community who regarded nurses as having servant status. I do not know what became of that squab, but I doubt whether the patient had it cooked for him. Much as I hate to admit it, I doubt if any of us would have gone the extra mile to cook a luxury for that particular man, had we had the time. If he did not get what he wanted a few instants after he rang his bell, he did not hestitate to throw anything he could get his hands on at the door of the room; this included his pitcher of water.

The first external hemorrhage I ever saw was at Massachusetts General. The man had been my patient previously on a lower floor, and his face had been operated on. It was a frightening experience to see the blood spurting from the artery. He was an Italian and was yelling at the top of his lungs. I gave him a towel to hold against his face and ran to telephone the doctor. In short order we had him on his way to the operating room. I accompanied him. When I came back into the ward, the men cheered me and said that they were going to give me a leather medal. What for, I do not know, but perhaps because I kept my wits.

The Children's Hospital students seemed to know more about putting on plaster of paris casts than some of the interns. I remember one instance in which an intern was struggling to put on a cast from toe to knee. I had to teach him the rudiments of applying a cast. Between us we got the cast on, and he was very grateful for his lesson.

I have very fond memories of my affiliation at the Massachusetts General Hospital. The supervisors were helpful and understanding about the adjustments we had to make. I learned much about the behavior of adults when they are ill, and I found that if you knew how to care for a sick child you knew how to think for the adult who could not express his needs. We had good teaching, and many of our lectures were given in the old ether dome where the first public demonstration of the use of ether in surgery took place on October 16, 1846.

As an alumna of the Children's Hospital School of Nursing, I was greatly disappointed when its twenty-one-year affiliation (1901-1922) with the Massachusetts General School of Nursing was discontinued. Had I been Director of the School at that time, I believe I would have urged that it be retained, because I believe that the experience was much broader at the Massachusetts General than it was then at the Peter Bent Brigham Hospital, which was limited to general medicine and surgery. Of course, at that time the Children's and Peter Bent Brigham had a number of interlocking relationships, as they have now.

Obstetrical Nursing

On September 30, 1919, Katharine Hitchcock and I went to New York to begin our affiliation in obstetrical nursing at the Manhattan Maternity Hospital, 59th and First Avenue. We were assigned to room together and had gone to bed the first night, when shortly afterwards — probably about 10:30 — the door opened and a flashlight was aimed at each bed. No one spoke and the door closed. About five o'clock in the morning there was pounding on our door, and a voice said, "High forceps in the delivery room at 6 a.m." I well remember saying to Katie, "Well they can have the delivery without me," and we stayed in bed for another hour. We learned shortly that any time there was a delivery, we were expected to attend. A bell was sounded and one had to drop whatever she was doing — even though she were bathing a patient — because the "State Board required" that every student see at least a given number of deliveries. The high forceps did not take place that first morning, but we were all summoned at eight o'clock, because it had been decided to do a Caesarean. Thus were we introduced to obstetrical nursing.

About the flashlight. It seems that one of the students shortly before had committed what the hierarchy there considered the unforgivable sin of staying out after ten without a pass and getting into the nurses' residence surreptitiously. All rooms were checked nightly thereafter. (I was not pleased, to say the least, to be waked up one night and asked where my roommate was. She was on night duty, and I thought they ought to have known it.) The student culprit was suspended, and her fellow students from the Presbyterian greatly resented the punishment. Shortly after the suspension, she became ill and died, and although this illness had no relation to her suspension, her death did not help her fellow students to have any good feeling about their affiliation with the hospital.

The nurse administrator ruled that institution with an iron hand. Her assistant was known as "Whispering Mary," for one never heard her coming but suddenly you heard a whispered comment about what you were doing. The powers that be were great on precision. The pins in breast binders were put in vertically and had to be in a straight row with no space between one pin and the next. One thing appalled me: ward patients had no mattresses on their beds, but private patients did. On the ward beds an army blanket was stretched taut across a wire spring and pinned with huge safety pins. Then followed a heavy, coarse, unbleached cotton sheet, and this was also pinned. A draw sheet of similar material was folded several times to go under the patient's buttocks. This could be changed when the need was great, but the under sheet was put on in the original making, and there it stayed until the patient was discharged at the end of ten days. Bed pans and other enamel utensils were rinsed after use and then put in a bathtub of carbolic acid solution — I have a vague recollection it was about two percent. When we needed a utensil we fished it out with an iron hook. Once a week the solution was changed by a student nurse.

Night duty hours were seven p.m. to seven a.m. with two hours off during the night. During the hours off, we were not allowed to return to the nurses' residence but went to a small sitting room on one of the floors of the hospital and stretched ourselves out on the floor. The student who was the "float" had to prepare the supper. The assignment as float was supposed to be something special. While I was float, I had two experiences which to me were typical of the undemocratic spirit of the place. One evening just before I was to go on duty, I was called to the director's office and told that I was to put on a fresh uniform, etc. as I was to "special" the chief of staff's daughter who was coming in for delivery. She was having a special nurse who could not get there until late in the evening. When I arrived at the floor where the patient was, there were the superintendent of the hospital, the superintendent of nurses, and the night supervisor. The administrator looked me all over and tried duly to impress on me who my patient was. What a to-do! The patient and I got along well, and several times I was called to the telephone by the superintendent to talk to the patient's father. When the patient finally arrived in the operating room, she was very much upset by the shrieks of a ward patient in another room. It did not take the resident house officer long to order a narcotic for the ward patient! And the preparation in the delivery room was too long to suit the doctor's daughter. Believe me, the routine was changed after that.

One night about ten o'clock, a woman appeared who was quite obviously in labor. Since she was "off the street," as they said, meaning that she was not a clinic patient, she was delivered in a small emergency room. Immediately after the delivery I was instructed to give her a bath and the skin preparation routine usual before delivery. The poor woman was exhausted. It seemed to me cruel that she was not allowed to have at least some rest. But routine was routine there, and she could not be transferred to the ward until she had the bath, etc. When she was being discharged on the tenth day, I was having my "two hours off" (we were on day duty from seven a.m. to seven p.m.). I was called to the office and asked where I had put the woman's fur. I replied, "In the locker with the rest of her clothes." "Well, it is not there, and you will have to go to the basement and find it." I remembered the fur perfectly well, for the night watchman who had gone to the basement with me when I was putting her clothes away had made a joke about the "old black cat." I couldn't find the fur and so reported.

I was one of the students who was fortunate enough to have a month at the 79th Street Station of the Henry Street Settlement. We returned to the hospital for classes. On one of these occasions I was asked to go to the office of the superintendent of nurses. And this was the con-

[17]

versation. "The other day Miss C—— received a gift of clothes, including a nice fur. She says that since you were responsible for the loss of a fur, she is willing to give you this fur piece to take to the woman. Otherwise you might have to replace it." I said, "I shall not replace the fur; neither shall I take this fur piece to the woman on the grounds that I lost her fur piece. When a hospital provides lockers which cannot be locked and instructs a student to place a patient's clothes in one of them, it is the hospital's responsibility, not the student's, if an article is lost. However, I shall be happy to take the fur to the woman, but only because I am sorry she lost her fur here." And I never heard another word on the subject. I have often wondered if the woman got the fur piece. Frequently after I graduated I used to see the former superintendent at national meetings, and if she had anyone with her, she would introduce them and tell them the story, which she apparently enjoyed. And each time the story lost nothing in the telling. I really think she was glad to see someone "stand up" to Miss C——. Remember, I was not a teen-ager or just twenty-one, but a mature woman of thirty-three.

Just before I completed the affiliation, I was again asked to remain after class, because the nurse administrator wanted to see me. To my amazement, I was invited into her sitting room. She began her conversation with "A little bird told me that you had made fun of ——. I know she doesn't speak the King's English, but she is a very good nurse." Then I remembered that a head nurse had griped to me that when she was off duty and this other head nurse had relieved for her, the latter proceeded to tell her she did not like the way she did some things. I had said, "Well, Miss R——, you know you don't never do it that way no how," which was the instruction given to us by this head nurse when she was illustrating how we should take a bottle of a baby's formula from the rack. It had become a sort of comment with us. This woman was an excellent nurse, but she retained some of the Pennsylvania Dutch of her forbears. My comment on the tale of the little bird was, "I think the little bird had little to do to repeat it," and I agreed with her about the kind of nurse this woman was. Then followed on the administrator's part a defense of not having well-prepared instructors because she could not get them. All this was preliminary to asking me to return as an instructor following my graduation. I could have told her why they had such a turnover of personnel, but I merely replied that I was entering Teachers College to become a well-prepared instructor. Good obstetrics were practiced in that hospital, and I enjoyed the experience in obstetrical nursing, but I did not enjoy the administrative atmosphere, and I think that was the feeling shared by most of the students. I could write a chapter of stories about Manhattan Maternity, including some of the pranks we played on the poor old ward maid who was not too bright. The Manhattan Maternity Hospital was closed some years ago, and its service was incorporated into the New York Hospital.

The month's experience on the District was thoroughly enjoyable and vitalizing. The chief supervisor at the 79th Street Station was Alta Dines, a charming woman, thoroughly democratic, and a good teacher and administrator. I had many associations with her later in national nursing affairs. Part of the experience included night calls. Usually the patients were clinic patients, and medical students were on call. Occasionally the family had their own physician. The student nurse usually arrived first, and the medics usually made themselves comfortable in easy chairs or on a couch, if there were any, while the student nurse followed the process of labor. It was a little scary going to the car line in the middle of the night, although sometimes the husband of the patient accompanied one. Later, a night supervisor began to accompany the students, after several students had been invited into cars by strange men.

The 79th Street Station was the branch of Henry Street Settlement where we lived. I can tell funny tales also about the English woman who was in charge. It was considered a great honor to be invited to sit at her table. We did not regard it as such. We enjoyed the living there and were glad that we had not had to go down to the residence on the waterfront where many of the other students who preceded us lived. They told stories of contact with rats and bed bugs.

I have discussed Manhattan Maternity in some detail, because I think that situation was typical of the attitudes of some of the early nurse administrators.

Finally a Diploma

I entered the Children's Hospital School of Nursing on December 9, 1915, and my diploma is dated January 21, 1920. Thereby hangs a tale. Shortly before the graduation exercises were to be held in May for the Class of 1919, the director of the school, Elizabeth E. Sullivan, went over my attendance record with me and said that with one week's vacation that summer, instead of two, and with no more illness I would graduate with the Class of 1919 and get my diploma on December 29, two days before my affiliation at the Manhattan Maternity Hospital was completed. I participated in the graduation exercises on May 22, 1919, and received a signed but undated diploma, as did the other students. That summer I made plans to enter Teachers College, Columbia, in the spring semester.

Imagine my surprise and chagrin when the new director who came in the fall told me my graduation date was January 21. "Theirs not to question why, theirs is but to do." Had she gone over the record with me, the error might have been found. The only thing that bothered me was that my application for Teachers College was due January 5 and I could register only as a graduate nurse. Here is the way the dilemma was solved as shown on my record: "On account of her excellent work, and because Teachers College will not admit her this February unless she is registered as a graduate nurse Miss Goostray is to be given her diploma January 5, two weeks and two days early. This is with the understanding that she continue her education at Teachers College." This note sounds as though I was through on January 5. Not so. The time was to be made up. When I got my diploma it was dated January 21. The irony of the situation was that three weeks were spent in the x-ray and photography department, doing work that had

[20]

no relation to nursing, and filling in a vacancy caused by the resignation of a paid employee.

It turned out that in the last few weeks of Miss Sullivan's directorship, she had the two instructors in their spare time transfer the personal records of the students to new cards. Miss Sullivan, a very meticulous person, wanted to leave things in ship-shape order. When I examined my card, on which a code system was used for assignments and time, an entry "iL" which meant one lower, a medical ward, mistakenly was entered under "Personal" rather than in the column for medical experience. Had I been ill, and I was not, the entry would have been IL.

The seven-day vacation allowance not credited to me and sixteen days of "Medical" copied under "Personal" accounted for the twenty-three days between December 29, when I had expected to graduate, and January 21, the new date given to me. Well, I suppose errors will occur, but no more codes were used after I got going as director. I have always maintained, and shall continue to maintain, that I am a member of the Class of 1919.

Incidentally, the certificate received from the Manhattan Maternity Hospital testifies that "Stella Goostray has completed the established course of three months instruction and practice in the Training School for Nurses of this institution. New York, May 1, 1920." It is a large diploma bearing a gorgeous red seal and four signatures. That "instruction and practice" was completed on December 31, 1919. Such is the accuracy of some records.

Reference

1. Goostray, Stella. *Fifty Years, A History of the School of Nursing, Children's Hospital, Boston.* The Alumnae Association, Boston, Mass. 1941, pp. 33-36.

Chapter Two

TEACHERS COLLEGE

MARY NORCROSS and I went to Teachers College for the spring semester, 1920, and lived in Bancroft Hall, intending to stay only for that one semester, since my cash was running low. Miss Nutting was the Director of the Department of Nursing and taught the would-be administrators, of which Mary M. Roberts was one; Isabel Stewart headed the instructors group, and Lillian Hudson was in charge of public health nursing. The classes were small in those days, and we knew most of our fellow students. I look forward to reading the history of the Department recently presented as a doctoral dissertation.

I was not in any of Miss Nutting's classes during that first semester, and she was away during the next year. She met with all the students at intervals, and (what amazed me) she called me by name when we met in the corridor. Miss Nutting evidently reviewed all applications for admission. I was very impressed when she said to me at the tea for incoming students, "I noticed from your application that you entered a school of nursing at about the same age I did and also that you did editorial work. We need people in nursing who can write, and I hope that you will remember that." And I, who had thought my writing days were over, within a comparatively few years was caught in the writing net when I got involved in Committees of the NLNE, and especially those of which Isabel Stewart was chairman. As yet I have not entirely wangled out.

Dean James E. Russell, the man who had opened the doors of Teachers College to nursing, was still there, as were other men like John Dewey, William Kilpatrick and Edward L. Thorndike, whose views on the philosophy of education and educational methods had focused the attention of educators on Teachers College. Dr. Thorndike was developing psychological tests, and when volunteers were asked for, I remember spending two Saturdays taking the psychological tests which he had devised. His report sent to each of us, showing where we stood in relation to the group tested and to adult women in general, noted that the test "measured intellect as it operates with ideas and symbols and abstract relations."[1]

We had an excellent course in chemistry with Charlotte Francis, and although it was largely a repeat of the course at Simmons, Miss Francis would give no exemptions. For the classes in anatomy and physiology and materia medica we went to the Columbia Medical School. Sister Domitilla was one of our classmates, and the instructor in anatomy regarded her as his star student. Our friendship with Sister Domitilla was renewed when she was a member of the Committee on the Grading of Nursing Schools. On the basis of the course at Simmons College we were exempted from bacteriology. After Professor Broadhurst looked over my notes and laboratory notebook and quizzed me a bit, she remarked, "It is too bad you don't remember more after such an excellent course."

Some of the courses outside of the nursing department bored me, and certainly we all got tired of being told about the deficiencies of nurses — especially of hearing the story of the nurse who brought the professor's wife a grapefruit cut the wrong way. This was used as an illustration of lack of appreciation of a patient's needs. It was repeated so many times that some of us were ready to hurl the grapefruit at him.

The classes in principles of teaching nursing and the history of nursing taught by Isabel Stewart were good, but she too often kept us beyond the scheduled time. She supervised the practice teaching. I taught elementary materia medica, including drugs and solutions, at

St. Mary's Children's Hospital School of Nursing, New York. Miss Stewart would come in, unannounced, sit in a back row, her hat tilted on the back of her head, and pretend to read a magazine. This one semester fulfilled the practice teaching requirement.

The principal of St. Mary's School asked me to teach the second semester and be paid for it. Since it meant spending a whole morning between the travel time from 120th Street to 34th Street, and the time spent in the classroom, and answering students' questions, I said, "Yes at three dollars a session." The Sister Administrator thought that was an unreasonable price, and anyway she did "not think nurses needed so much teaching." (She herself was a graduate of Wellesley College.) I thought she was getting a bargain.

Instead of spending only one semester at Teachers College, I returned for another year since I had received an appointmnt as "Assisting Scholar in the Department of Nursing and Health," and a small Red Cross scholarship which helped out with finances. My work was with Isabel Stewart, looking up reference material for classes, filing reference material and doing other odd jobs. In the spring semester I taught drugs and solutions to five five-year students who were in the joint program of Presbyterian Hospital School of Nursing and Teachers College.

Isabel Stewart kept urging me to return and complete the requirements for the baccalaureate degree. During the six years I was at the Philadelphia General Hospital School of Nursing, which followed the year and a half at Teachers College, I sandwiched in a few courses at the University of Pennsylvania. It was practically next door to the Hospital. These courses included an advanced course in chemistry and one in American history, others in ethics, logic, psychology, mythology, and a delightful course in Irish literature. I knew I had enough credits for a baccalaureate degree, but one had to take some final courses at Teachers College, so I commuted for the fall semester, 1925, to fulfill the requirement. When the final toll was taken there were six extra credits which could be credited for a master's degree, and they were used later at Boston University. The baccalaureate degree was conferred in 1926, "in absentia." During the spring of 1926 I took two courses at the University of Pennsylvania, and since I wanted to submit a full transcript to Teachers College, and had to have it in by a certain date, I asked for early rating on these courses. In order to get that early rating I had to accept a "passing grade." The University gave three ratings — D, Distinguished, G, Good and P, Passing. So I swallowed my pride and accepted. I believe the professors never bothered to look at the examination papers.

Reference

1. Report on Intelligence Test as given by Edward L. Thorndike.

Chapter Three

"DEAR OLD BLOCKLEY" — MY FIRST POST

O N the advice of Isabel Stewart I accepted a position as instructor of science at the Philadelphia General Hospital School, to which the old name "Blockley" and some of its ways still clung. The school had a large student body, and, in addition, received affiliating students from many small hospitals in Pennsylvania. Students also came from the Army School of Nursing, and during my term as Educational Director, Lulu Wolf Hassenplug was one of them. And she was just as full of creative ideas then as she has been during her years in the forefront of nursing education.

Sarah Lillian Clayton, or, as she was always called, S. Lillian Clayton, was Director of the School and of Nursing Service. She had been President of the National League of Nursing Education, and currently was a member of the Rockefeller Committee to Study Nursing Education, and President of the American Journal of Nursing Company. In 1926, she became President of the American Nurses' Association.

I was interviewed for the position of instructor by the Educational Director, under whom I was to work, and met Miss Clayton for the first time at her conference the first morning of my employment in September, 1921. That morning I appeared at breakfast wearing white shoes and stockings, but Gertrude Maloney, the supervisor of the pediatric unit, who had been at the Children's with me and later was one of my associates there, quickly tipped me off that Miss Clayton wore black shoes and stockings, and that her assistants (I fitted into that category) were supposed to do likewise. A hurried change into black shoes and stockings and my first day was saved from embarrassment on that score.

I was not there too long before I realized that I might be in the right church but in the wrong pew. Every move had to be first referred to the Educational Director. There was no opportunity for creative teaching. No one in the department was allowed to open the files. I was assigned to teach classes to which I had not agreed (for example, bandaging) and makeup classes for students which the Educational Director was supposed to teach. Some of the seniors had to have classes which belonged in their Junior year. She was what I called an "unorganized person" and could not delegate authority. The last straw came when I was scheduled to teach some makeup classes on Christmas Day.

I went to see Miss Clayton and asked to be relieved in time to enter Teachers College for the second semester. Miss Clayton told me that I could not resign in the middle of the school year. Then she "let down her hair" and told me that my story of unsatisfactory relations with the Educational Director was only one of several such stories, and each time it happened the excuse given by the Educational Director was that the person was not prepared for the job. Well, I was, and Miss Clayton had purposely let the Educational Director interview me. The outcome of the matter was that I resigned for the end of the year intending to go back to Teachers College. Somewhat later, Miss Clayton told me that she had the resignation of the Educational Director and asked me to stay on as an instructor. I ended up with the appointment as Educational Director, and for five years there was an opportunity to do some constructive work. With the exception of a new instructor who did not fit in well and only stayed one year (she was replaced by Mary E. Norcross), the faculty was a happy family. Not only did we work in harmony, but we played together. I remember those associates and the administrative assistants in Miss Clayton's office with great affection. The latter had had their troubles from the same source as I. Loretta Johnson taught the principles and practice of nursing over a number of years, and succeeded Miss Clayton as Director of the School. Dora Mathis was a science instructor and later held a number of important positions in various parts of the country and in Peking. She was also Director of the Episcopal Hospital School of Nursing at Philadelphia when she retired. She died a few years ago, and an award given in Pennsylvania is named in her honor. I looked on her as a beloved younger sister.

Those were busy days, but we had plenty of energy then. We worked a long week, with a half-day a week and every other Sunday off. All of the instructors, including myself, visited the wards almost daily. It was a bit frustrating to see students taking short cuts and not doing the procedures as they were taught. Miss Clayton and I talked about this once, and she said something like this to me: "Remember these students will not always work under the conditions we have here in a large, understaffed city hospital. They are being taught good nursing care, and I believe they will give it." The head nurses on the wards were faced with innumerable and difficult problems, but they were all women of great dedication to the welfare of patients.

Although the few classrooms were good, the laboratory well-equipped, and the library above average for the times, we were hampered by their limitations because of the large number of students. The September section more often than not numbered about one hundred. The students had various degrees of education, from one or two years of high school to college degrees. One great lack was office space. The Educational Director had the only adequate office. But we made do.

We had two Chase dolls and a baby doll. When requisition after requisition failed to bring us another adult size doll, we made one. We stuffed a union suit and then applied plaster of paris over it. I have forgotten what we used for the head, but someone painted the face and hair. And believe it or not we inserted test tubes in the proper places so that irrigations and enemas could be given. After Dr. Doane saw our home-made Mrs. Chase, he did buy us another, but we did not give up our creation.

I doubt if the teaching in many schools of that day surpassed that of the Philadelphia General Hospital School. Practically all the lecturers were chiefs of staff and held teaching positions at Jefferson Medical School or the University of Pennsylvania Medical School. Patients were brought from the wards, appropriate lantern slides and blown-up charts were thrown on a screen. Fresh and preserved specimens came from pathology, and cultures from the bacteriology laboratory.

Dr. Joseph Doane, the administrator of the hospital, who also had an appointment at the University Medical School, took his turn on service in the medical wards and conducted teaching rounds. He also taught the student nurses. He gave the medical lectures, and I set up the demonstrations for him. On the morning of the lecture, I went to his office and we reviewed together what we would do in class. The "nature fakir," he was wont to call me. I still remember my feeling the first time he asked me to cut open a heart — an item on the agenda he had omitted to tell me about beforehand.

I left the Philadelphia General at about the time the new building program was started. There was a general clearing out, and the city held an auction. Dr. Doane had discovered several sets of plated sugars and creamers with the initials B. A. H. (Blockley Alms House). He had someone bid them in for him, and one of my treasured possessions is one of these sets given to me by Dr. and Mrs. Doane. A friend had it resilvered for me, and it is beautiful.

Dr. Eldridge L. Eliason, Professor of Surgery at the University, who was always harping on "too much class work," nevertheless did teach, and also served on the School of Nursing Committee. "Keep them at the bench; that's what they need." Another of his oft-repeated remarks was "A patient in a hospital today has no more chance than a snowball in hell." Several years after I left Philadelphia, he invited me to be his co-author of a book on surgical nursing, but there were then too many fish in the pan to throw in another.

We had one lecturer who might be termed a "character." He taught pathology, and if any of the specimens to be shown did not quite suit him he walked out. One time he requested that a pair of kidneys be provided for each four students. Well, the department of pathology could not supply that number. And so when he came and found his order had not been filled, out he went. Another time he requested that we obtain from the abattoir the gastro-intestinal tract (intact) of a pig. Did he get it? He did. The instructor in anatomy and I went to the abattoir for it!

We were very close to the students in those days. Each year, the seniors published a class book, *Scope,* in which they had great fun spoofing instructors. One year the instructors decided to put out a parody of their *Scope,* and so we prepared a little mimeographed booklet in which we noted that for some years it had been the custom for the Senior class to make notes other than those on the lectures being given. Afterwards, these appeared in a class book, and we, as instructors, read about ourselves as the students saw us. All our pet phrases and brilliant "idears" were handed down to posterity. We dedicated our booklet to those "with whom we struggled early and labored long, but whom we held, and would always hold, in affectionate remembrance."

As Educational Director, I continued to teach the courses in drugs and solutions, as outlined in the Standard Curriculum, and in chemistry, but I did not find current texts to my liking. So I decided to write new ones based on the notes made during a number of years of teaching the subjects. The text *Drugs and Solutions* went through two editions under that title, was then revised to meet the suggestions in the 1927 League Curriculum, and appeared as *Introduction to Materia Medica: Drugs and Solutions,* for two more editions. Again, there was a change of emphasis to mathematics, and the last edition, under the title *Mathematics and Measurement in Nursing Practice* appeared in 1963. A few royalties still come in.

I knew Walter G. Karr, Chief Chemist, Laboratories of the Philadelphia General Hospital, Assistant Professor of Biochemistry, Graduate School of Medicine, University of Pennsylvania, and married to one of the graduates of the School of Nursing. I asked him if he would be interested in writing a simple text on chemistry with me, and he said that he would. The modest little volume, with no illustrations but including a laboratory manual and a few line drawings of apparatus, appeared in 1924 under the title *Applied Chemistry for Nurses*. Dr. Karr died in 1946. The ninth edition of what started as Goostray-Karr and now is Goostray-Schwenck's *A Textbook in Chemistry* came out in 1966. It was my swan song in chemistry.

I noted recently a statement that Dr. L. Jean Bogert wrote the first chemistry for nurses, a statement which needs some qualifying. The Goostray-Karr came out at about the same time, but neither of these was the first chemistry that had been prepared especially for nurses.

Following World War I, the Rockefeller Foundation had developed a program to establish modern schools of nursing in Europe, in cooperation with national governments. Miss F. Elizabeth Crowell, whose office was in Paris, was responsible for this program. Young graduates from Poland came to the Philadelphia General for a year of clinical experience and instruction, and one came also from Alsace-Lorraine. Later, Brazil was added to the list, and one young woman, socially well prepared, came for the three-year course in order that she might take leadership in Brazil. And she did in many capacities. She was Edith Fraenkel, whose last position before retirement was that of Director of the University School in Sao Paulo. She was the representative of the Brazil Nurses' Association when it was received into the International Council of Nurses. Miss Crowell in 1923 invited me to take the directorship of the Ana Nery School in Rio de Janeiro, but I did not accept.

There were many visitors to the Hospital and School from other countries as well as the United States. They stayed anywhere from a few days to several weeks, and spent most of the time in the educational department. It was very time-consuming, but we enjoyed having them. A number of them came from England. Miss Derbyshire of the University Hospital and Miss Monk of the London Hospital were among the first. Later, Miss Lloyd Still from St. Thomas's came. Miss Norcross and I had a car, so it was part of our responsibility to take the visitors to visit the historical shrines around Philadelphia. On one occasion, we were at Valley Forge with some English visitors, and a guide who was showing us around said, "Here is where we licked the British." It gave us a little kick. And we always, believe it or not, introduced those staid British matrons to ice cream cones.

Many of our visitors requested copies of the nursing procedures in use which were then in mimeographed form. It seemed a feasible idea to have them printed and have the volume sold. With Miss Clayton's blessing, the procedures were edited and printed in a volume dedicated to Alice Fisher, a graduate of the Nightingale School at St. Thomas's Hospital, London, and the founder of the Philadelphia General Hospital School of Nursing. There is no note in the first edition (April, 1924) as to the editor. However, I did indicate the editor in the second edition published May 18, 1927. I quote here that note, signed "S. G."

> This book represents the work of all who had been concerned with the teaching of student nurses in the Philadelphia General Hospital during many years, in the classroom and ward alike. While primarily intended for student nurses and graduates of this school, it has found its way into many other hands in this country and abroad, and with necessary modifications has been translated into Russian and Chinese.
>
> The second edition appears coincident with the laying of the cornerstone of the new Philadelphia General Hospital. It has been thoroughly revised to meet changing needs, but an effort has been made to preserve that spirit in which this school began, which bade its students . . .
> 'Enter to learn, Go out to serve.'[1]

A reference to the index of the book, a copy of the first edition of which is in the Nursing Archive, Mugar Library, Boston University, will show many nursing procedures unheard of in these days, such as wet and dry cupping and the application of cantharides plasters and other types of counter-irritants. Although the directions are not given in the procedure book, every "probationer" had to make a pneumonia jacket out of cotton batting.

To be the director of nursing (she was called chief nurse) in a

municipal hospital of the size of the Philadelphia General was no easy
job, and when Lillian Clayton came to the hospital, it still had many
of the ways of Old Blockley. One of the things I shall always remember about her was her concern about the care of patients. There were
areas in the hospital which grieved her greatly, including the Department for Mental Patients, which adjoined the main hospital and of
which she was the director of nursing. She was an unemotional person, but I saw her once after she had come from a visit to that part
of the hospital when she put her head down on her desk and cried.
Certainly primitive conditions that were reminiscent of the old time
care, or better said, lack of care, of psychiatric patients still existed.

Miss Clayton was a graduate of the Philadelphia General and had
worked in Ohio with Ella Phillips Crandall, who was her closest
friend. She was Educational Director at the Illinois Training School
for Nurses, and served also at the Minneapolis General Hospital School
of Nursing. She was a reserved person, gracious in manner, and
seemed to have few intimate friends outside of the profession. She was
held in high respect by nurses throughout the country. She and Susan
Francis were good friends, but I never heard them call each other by
their Christian names. Miss Clayton was fond of going to the theatre,
and she always dressed well.

There is a photograph of Miss Clayton (it was used in connection with the newspaper account of the posthumous awarding of the
Saunders Medal) which portrays her as "tight lipped" but she seldom
looked that way. Occasionally, she would ask one of her associates to
do something, and if she hesitated, there would come the tight lips
and the remark, "Well, I will do it myself." And, of course, the other
did it. Miss Clayton could be stern, occasionally forbidding, and severe in discipline, especially when there was any violation of liquor
regulations by students or graduates, but I have seldom seen a more
tender person than she when a young student nurse was really in
trouble.

Miss Clayton was within a few weeks of completing her term of
office in the American Nurses' Association, when she became ill and
died after a few days' illness. Her funeral service was held in the liv-

ing-room of the Alice Fisher Home, and professional friends came from long distances. The body was then placed on a caisson, and we followed it on foot through the lane between the University of Pennsylvania buildings and those of the Philadelphia General Hospital to Woodland Cemetery where she was buried very near Alice Fisher.

A memorial service for Miss Clayton was held at the ANA convention in Milwaukee shortly after her death. Annie W. Goodrich gave the memorial address. Miss Clayton was posthumously awarded the first Walter B. Saunders Award.

My days at the Philadelphia General Hospital are remembered with gratitude because of the privilege of working with Miss Clayton, her associates and the head nurses on the various services, and also because of the happy relationship with hundreds of student nurses.

An interesting account of the early days of the training school at Blockley appeared in the *Bulletin* of the Alumnae Association of the Philadelphia General Hospital School of Nursing, in December, 1961.[2] The name of its author is not given. The account was written either by Roberta West, who was in the first class, or by someone who heard her recount these early days. I lean to the first author. Many times when I was at the Philadelphia General, I heard Miss West tell of those early days.

According to the records at the Philadelphia General Hospital School of Nursing, Roberta West entered the training school on January 7, 1885, and was graduated in January, 1886. A gold medal for outstanding achievement had been established, and Roberta West received the first one. The custom continues.

At the time I was in Philadelphia, Miss West was secretary of the Pennsylvania State Board of Nurse Examiners. She often came to have lunch with Miss Clayton in her apartment, and I was usually invited also. She was a rare character, a tall, raw-boned individual, with a caustic tongue. She used to like to twit me about coming from Boston. I once reminded her that one of her heroes, Benjamin Franklin, also came from Boston. But she got the better of me by her retort, "Yes, but as soon as he was old enough to know much, he left Boston and came to Philadelphia."

Mention is made in this *Bulletin* of historical articles being prepared by Ernestine Kittl D'Estel, familiarly known as "Kittl." She was a lovable individual who was one of the so-called "second assistants" in Miss Clayton's office. It would be hard to define her duties, but if anyone wanted something and did not know the ropes about getting it, she was told to "Ask Kittl." She came from Prague as a very young woman, entered the training school, and never left it until her retirement. That retirement was short. She met an untimely death, with several members of her family, from seepage of carbon monoxide from the garage into the house where they were asleep.

The *Bulletin* also mentions the burial of Miss Fisher in Woodland Cemetery, which was just back of the Hospital. It was a custom when I was at the School for faculty and students to march in procession to the cemetery on the afternoon of Easter, each carrying a white carnation which was laid on Miss Fisher's grave.

References

1. *Procedure Book*, Philadelphia General Hospital School of Nursing. 2nd ed. 1927.

2. *Bulletin*. Alumnae Association, Philadelphia General Hospital School of Nursing. December, 1961.

Chapter Four

HOME AGAIN IN BOSTON

EARLY in the spring of 1926, I was asked to return to the Children's Hospital School of Nursing as an instructor for a year, and at the end of that period to assume directorship of the school and nursing service. Having been the Director of Education in a school whose student body numbered almost three times as many as did the Children's Hospital School, and involved in the nursing problems of a large municipal hospital, it seemed hardly necessary for me to accept the status of an instructor. I had also agreed to stay on for the next school year where I was. And so a year before I was to take charge of the school, I received the appointment to assume the position at the Children's Hospital on August 1st, 1927, and was given authority to make plans for the coming year regarding appointments of my immediate associates and changes in organization of staff. My appointment also included responsibility for the nursing at the Infants' Hospital, a separate corporation.

There were difficult times to go through those first few months, with some inherited problems and others that came along of which the students never knew, nor did some of the faculty, for that matter. There are some paths which an administrator of a school must walk alone. I am sure some of the older students in the school thought they were being given a hard life, but they were giving me one, too. I clamped down on them, because some of them were going "high, wide, and handsome." The aunt of one student went to Miss Smith, the administrator of the hospital, to complain that some of the students were unhappy about the new rules. A few months later the aunt apologized to me and said that the students had changed their minds. Perhaps when I accepted the challenge of a student on Halloween to duck for an apple — and got it — they decided I might pass.

Some of the pranks of the students were harmless enough. It happened more than once that a telephone call came from a young man who called me by name and then asked, "How about a date tonight?" I am always sorry not to have accepted one of those invitations to have seen the reaction when I appeared downstairs.

As I have mentioned previously, I wore black shoes and stockings at the Philadelphia General and continued to do so when I went to the Children's. It never occurred to me that the students cared what I wore. They wore black shoes and stockings (and continue to do so in this year of 1968 of their own choice). But on the students' Christmas tree that first Christmas was a pair of old white shoes marked with my name. I took the hint and wore white footgear until, at the suggestion of George Meyer, who was then the administrator of the hospital, I discarded the white uniform and cap for a blue silk dress with a white silk collar, and no cap. Many of the older alumnae were not pleased at this change. However, I did don cap and white uniform for the graduation exercises and on other occasions. Nowadays, one seldom sees a director of a hospital school of nursing, at least in urban hospitals, wearing a white uniform. Another thing that bothered alumnae was that the students wore their caps on the back of their heads. I tried to move the caps forward but fought a losing battle most of the time.

Before I get down to more serious and important events in those first years as director of the school, I add this: there have been few times in my life when I was more touched than when one of the seniors who had been a thorn in the flesh with her pranks came to my office to say "good-bye" on the day she completed her course, put her arms around me, and kissed me.

Soon after I took office, plans for a building program began to take shape. The Board of Managers appointed a special committee, with George Meyer, secretary of the Board, to work with the administrator, the medical staff and the superintendent of nurses to study existing needs. The title "superintendent of nurses" has been used here, because conservative Boston clung to the old title. I shall use the term interchangeably with "director," but the official title used in the letter from the Board which came yearly giving me my reappointment was "Superintendent of Nurses and Principal of the School of Nursing." When I was notified by Mr. Farley, the Board president, after my retirement that an emeritus title had been given to me, the title was "Director Emeritus of the School of Nursing."

The building program included the remodeling of old buildings and the construction of new ones, including a residence for the nursing staff. Besides single rooms for all students, and some small suites for faculty, the residence included classrooms, offices for faculty, a professional and a small fiction library, an infirmary, a large recreation room in addition to the spacious living room, and a small sitting room with a diet kitchen on each floor. The nursing staff had been living in the old Harvard Hotel at the corner of Huntington Avenue and Longwood Avenue, and in some small houses on Longwood near the hospital. Vose House, the residence where we lived as students, had been taken over for a private ward. The housing situation was not conducive to my peace of mind. Trolleys screeched on the tracks all night on the front of the residence and frequently at the back at night there was yelling and loud talk indicating that a brawl was going on. It was not good to have students returning to the hospital (at least a five-minute walk along Longwood Avenue) at all hours of the night when they were on call for the operating room. We moved into the new residence, Gardner House, in May, 1930.

Any director of a school who thought there was no smoking by student nurses in the residence, in the late 'twenties, even though it was banned, was hiding her head in the sand. It used to disturb Miss Hall, at the Brigham, and myself to see student nurses in uniform from the several schools in the area, including our own, smoking in the drugstores and eating places at Longwood Avenue and Brigham Circle. We decided to face the situation head-on and to lift the ban on smoking in students' rooms in the nurses' residence, and we agreed to make the announcement when we moved into Gardner House. Miss Hall did not have the problem of a number of affiliating schools. I knew I was in for trouble from some of the schools as soon as they got my letter. One of the directors called me at the request of her Advisory Committee to ask me to see that their students did not smoke. I had seen them often smoking in the corner drugstore. I answered the request by asking, "Do you expect me to get a billy and a helmet and go sniffing around for smoke?" I was greatly amused when she called me a few days later (this was before the students knew the ban was to be lifted) to tell me that a neighbor had called their School of Nursing Office to report that some students were smoking on the roof of the hospital. The president of the student association was one of the culprits.

Others can evaluate more objectively than I the educational gains made in the Children's Hospital School of Nursing, but my efforts during the first years were directed towards improving the quality of nursing service and the education of student nurses by increasing the number of auxiliary workers and the number of graduate nurses employed for staff duty. Another objective was more participation by faculty, other than the director and her two assistants, in decisions affecting students and in reviewing their progress. I also wanted less emphasis on a "probationary period" and more on students as in the "first term, first year." We discarded the pink probationer's uniform the first year because it was an added student expense not justified by the length of time it was worn, and it tended to set the students apart. Further comments on the development of the school may be found in the *Alumnae Bulletin* of 1937 and the *Fifty Years* history.[2]

I felt strongly that there should be more professional status for the faculty and recognition by the administration that they should attend local professional meetings and national conventions. No money was allotted to pay their expenses, but we did get authority later for their attendance. In all of these changes I had the backing of the Advisory Committee of the School of Nursing. When an assistant administrator checked me absent in her "time book" for an afternoon spent at a professional meeting, and I was "docked" for the time, there was a "show-down." I had gone to the Children's Hospital School of Nursing as a professional woman and would remain only if that were recognized. The practice of "docking" in similar cases was stopped.

There seemed to be no by-law of the Board which spelled out the functions of the Superintendent of Nurses and Principal of the School of Nursing. Consequently there was dabbling from several quarters. After I consulted with Mr. Meyer about the matter, an adequate by-law was added. Two incidents will indicate why I thought this was necessary. One of the junior physicians who was supposed to give certain medical lectures met me casually and informed me that he had asked a certain man to give them in his place, and I informed him that I made those appointments. When several new departments were to be opened, and one especially needed an unusual type of person with sound educational background as head nurse, I asked the chief where he would suggest that the person I had selected could go for some added experience and teaching. He told me that he had already made the appointment with the consent of the administrator. Well, that soon got straightened out, and the day came when the chief thanked me for my choice.

The medical staff had requested that the number of affiliating students be reduced and there be an increase in Children's Hospital students. The Executive Committee of the Board invited me to discuss the matter. The point of view presented to them was, first, the number of students in a school should not exceed the number for which its smallest basic service could provide equal experience, and second, since the Children's Hospital drew many patients from a large area and it was impossible for the local hospital, if it had a school, to meet the requirements for pediatric nursing of the State Board of Nurse Examiners, we had a community responsibility to meet. The number of affiliating students was not reduced, but rather increased.

We made some changes in the experiences offered to the affiliating students, to the mutual advantage of them and our own students. We were then receiving from some affiliating schools students who had not graduated from high school. The affiliating schools were notified that we would receive no student for affiliation who was not a high school graduate and who was admitted to their schools after September 1, 1930. This action helped to raise Massachusetts' standards for entrance to schools of nursing.

The former director of the school told me that she had never had an opportunity to meet with the Board of Directors or its Executive Committee. I had numerous opportunities and found the Board open-minded and cooperative when valid reasons were given for the requests being made.

For ten years I tried to get a change in the requirement for operating room experience imposed by the New York Board of Regents. Their reply was always the same: "This is what we require in children's hospitals." There seemed to be no evaluation of the experience being offered in the various hospitals or of what were the essential values of operating room experience. I gave them the evidence as to what two hospitals in their own state offered in operating room experience as contrasted with the diversified experience in the Children's Hospital, Boston. But to no avail.[3] After ten years of alibis, the New York Board broke down, and no operating room experience other than that within the Children's Hospital was required for Children's Hospital students. It amuses me to consider how little emphasis is placed on operating room experience for students today.

On January 1, 1930, I began a seven-month leave of absence to work with the Committee on the Grading of Nursing Schools. I returned for a long weekend each month to catch up on problems at the Children's, but my able assistants, Mary E. Norcross and Gertrude Maloney, kept things running smoothly.

Added Responsibilities

The nursing service in the private ward was not under the superintendent of nurses, but had a supervisor who was directly responsible to the administrator. There were no student nurses in that department. The Out-Patient Department also had a director, and although students were assigned there, it was almost as though they were on affiliation. Later, I was asked to take the responsibility of the nursing in the private ward and in the Out-Patient Department.

There did not seem to be any encouragement to have guests at the Children's School of Nursing, such as we had had at the Philadelphia General. I finally broke the ice by suggesting to the Advisory Committee that we ought to invite some of the foreign nurses who were attending the International Congress of Nurses in Montreal (1929). The Committee acquiesced, although I do not think the administrator was too much in favor. One visitor, Athina Messolora from Athens, was a very influential person in nursing affairs and Red Cross activities as well as in social circles in Greece. I used to see her at the congresses of the International Council of Nurses, and afterwards I had a very happy reunion with her when we were in Athens at the end of our trip around the world (1964). Effie Taylor wrote her that she thought I was going to Athens at a certain time, and one can imagine my surprise when I was in an airline office to have someone say to me, "There is a telephone call for you." Certainly Miss Messolora knew all the ropes for finding people, and we were delightfully entertained by her. Another one of our visitors was a French nurse who taught me how to make onion soup, my one culinary accomplishment.

We continued to have guests, to our mutual advantage, once I had made a start, and after Mr. Meyer became the administrator there was never any question about it. These guests were usually sponsored by the Rockefeller Foundation.

A Thai student nurse was in the school when I came. She was sponsored by the father of the present King of Thailand, who was a doctor and then a student in the Harvard School of Public Health. After her return home, she became the director of the school in the municipal hospital of Bangkok and a leader in promoting modern nursing and nursing education in Thailand. During the first part of the thirties, the Rockefeller Foundation through Miss Mary Beard sent three young Thai women for their basic education at the Children's Hospital. They remained in this country for a year of post-graduate study, but continued to reside at Gardner House during that year. A fifth student then came and later prepared for public health nursing. All five of them made their contribution in nursing in their own country. All through the years, these five have kept in touch with me, and in 1964 Miss Norcross, who was assistant in education while they were in school, and I spent nearly a week in Bangkok. And what a reunion we had! We were wined and dined, chauffeured where we wanted to go, entertained in their homes, introduced to their families, and given a delightful reception by the Thailand Nurses' Association.

My relationships with the staff were good, and I could count on Dr. Blackfan, chief of the medical staff, and Dr. Ladd, chief of the surgical staff, to discuss matters with objectivity. Fortunately, there were few times when I had to confer with them or they with me about conflicts. Dr. Osgood, chief of the orthopedic staff, was also helpful. Dr. Ober, who succeeded him, was not as active within the hospital and there were few contacts with him. He once wrote me a letter about a private duty nurse who had asked him to write an order for morphine before she would give the dose, the time limit on the previous order having expired. My reply reminded him that the rule governing the situation was made by the general medical staff, and as long as I was director of nursing I would support any nurse who complied with it. I heard no more from him. After both Dr. Ober and I had retired, we sat next to each other at a dinner, and after the speeches about the accomplishments of the hospital and new plans, he turned to me and said, "Yes, and you and I helped to bring them about."

The War Years

Some of the young medical fry especially were a little hard to take during the war days. They did not seem to know there was a war.

And how I missed Dr. Blackfan, who would have straightened matters out. He was ill for some time and died in 1941. The Committee on Procurement and Assignment of the National Nursing Council had laid ground rules for civilian hospitals based on the essentiality of the service to be rendered, and these had been adopted by the Procurement and Assignment unit of the War Man Power Commission. One of these rules related to the use of private duty nurses only for seriously ill patients. Most of the private duty nurses (and they were mostly nurses not eligible for military service) played the game straight, but there were a few who did not abide by the rules. Each time one of these young medical men ordered a special nurse for a spoiled child who was not acutely ill and did not get the nurse, there was a visit to my office. One of them said to me, "Well, the mother managed to get one from another school," and my reply was, "I do not deal in the black market." Any child who needed special nursing at the Children's Hospital got it. We assigned one of our few staff nurses when we could not get a private duty nurse, and at no time throughout the war were limitations placed on admissions.

One of these mothers, who was on some sort of committee at the hospital, began a little campaign to get me "fired," but the move "back-fired," and she was the one out. At any rate, she was seen no more around the Children's Hospital. I could have sued her for slander on the basis of some of her tactics.

My responsibilities for national service naturally added responsibilities to my associates at the Children's, and the faculty to a person upheld my hands by their loyalty and support. I wish I could name them all, but that is dangerous to attempt since I might inadvertently omit someone. They all know they have my abiding affection and gratitude. And that goes for those, too, who during my tenure from the beginning, in office, in teaching department, and on the wards as supervisors and head nurses worked with me for a common goal — sound nursing education for the sake of the quality of nursing service and not for the sake of education in itself.

The close of the war brought with it many changes at the Children's Hospital. Mr. John Wells Farley, familiarly known as "Mike"

Farley, a distinguished, civic-minded man, well-known in Boston, became president of the Board. The so-called Board of Managers was relatively small in size and somewhat ingrown, since many of its members were the sons and grandsons of men who had served the Children's Hospital through many years. There was a recognized need for a much more broadly based directorate, and the Board of Trustees, as it was later called, became more representative of many groups of business and professional men. Mr. Farley had a great vision and the drive to give substance to the vision of a Children's Hospital Medical Center, which would have many diversified units for child care other than the existing Children's Hospital and Infants' Hospital, largely for acutely ill medical and surgical patients. Beginning in 1946, the Children's Hospital Medical Center became a reality, although, of course, not of the scope it is today.

Mr. George von L. Meyer resigned in 1945, and I missed him greatly. There were several interim directors for short periods before Dr. Charles Branch was appointed to the post in the latter part of 1945. Several chiefs of staff were due to be appointed in 1946. Dr. Charles Janeway became Medical Chief, Dr. Richard S. Smith having acted in the interim between Dr. Blackfan's death in 1941 and Dr. Janeway's appointment. Dr. Robert Gross, later to become an eminent heart surgeon known throughout the world, was to succeed Dr. Ladd, and Dr. W. T. Green was to follow Dr. Ober. Both Dr. Gross and Dr. Green had been at the Children's for a long time. They are still my friends today, as is Dr. Sidney Farber, who was made Director of Laboratories and Research. All three of these men, and Dr. Janeway as well, have made tremendous contributions to the health of children throughout the world.

My responsibilities during the war period as chairman of the National Nursing Council for War Service and the difficulties of keeping the nursing service adequate for good care at the Children's with a depleted staff left me depleted also. When I reviewed the many changes taking place within the hospital and the building plans being made, I decided after much consideration to retire in 1946. Although Mr. Farley and Dr. Branch tried to dissuade me, I did not change my mind.[4]

When Mr. Farley first became president, he had little idea of the differentiation between a nursing service and a school, or that certain functions relating to these should not come within the scope of the doctors' responsibilities, but were those of the Director of the School and Nursing Service. He soon "caught on" and I found him an understanding and sympathetic person.

After I left the School of Nursing, I was very careful not to get my fingers into any of its pies. Nothing is worse than a long-time director who hovers about thinking that after she leaves the school is going to destruction. If she only knew it, she is not very complimentary to herself. Under the leadership of Muriel B. Vesey, who had served as night supervisor, assistant in the office, and then as my associate in nursing service, and who had a sound philosophy of nursing education and nursing service, good judgment, and a superior quality of mind, the school would progress to meet changing needs. When asked for an opinion I gave it, but I never volunteered advice, and for months after my resignation I never went into the hospital or Gardner House. However, I got somewhat involved in 1951.

In late December, 1950, a proposal was made by the Peter Bent Brigham Board of Directors that the school of nursing there and that at the Children's be consolidated. There was much discussion on the part of the administrator at the Brigham about the continuing accreditation of Children's Hospital. Mr. Farley was disturbed by the picture portrayed by the administrator and asked if I would be willing to go to New York and confer with the Director of the National Accrediting Service. It happened that I was to go to New York in the afternoon of the day the telephone message came, and I agreed to see the director if possible. I did see her, and as my letter to Mr. Farley indicated, there was no policy at that time nor had it been suggested that the Accrediting Service discontinue the accreditation of a school in a special hospital then on the list so long as the school reasonably met the criteria used as a basis of evaluation as outlined in the Service's *Manual of Accrediting Educational Programs in Nursing*.[5]

Some weeks later, Mr. Farley asked me to accompany him to a meeting at which the consolidation was to be discussed. It was held in Mr. Robert Cutler's office, Mr. Cutler being the president of the Board at the Brigham. I suspect that Robert Cutler and the administrator of the Brigham were somewhat surprised to see me appear with Mr. Farley, who stated that I was representing the Children's Hospital as a consultant. The Brigham trustees had lined up Dr. R. Louise McManus and Lucille Petry, and of course they were "agin" schools in special hospitals. But they conceded voluntarily that the Children's had been, and was, a good school. It was surprising to me that neither the director of the Brigham School nor that of the Children's was at the meeting. After the meeting, I told Mr. Farley that the present director of the school should be present at all conferences on the school — that I would be glad to be of any help, but she was the person to attend the meetings. Well, the schools were not consolidated, and in this year of our Lord, 1968, the Children's Hospital School of Nursing is still going strong, is still on the accredited list of schools, and has been there since the first list was published in 1941.

In the spring of 1954, the Alumnae Association had my portrait painted by Pezzati, a well-known Boston artist who had studied with the eminent portrait painter, Charles Hopkinton. The latter came in a number of times during the sittings and made suggestions. When it was unveiled June 16, 1954, in Gardner House, where it now hangs in the living room, Claude Fuess, Ph.D., Director Emeritus of Andover Academy, a distinguished educator and biographer, was the presiding officer.

The following is what I said on that occasion:

Dr. Fuess, Mr. Howe, former students and colleagues in the school and hospital, and friends. Little did I think on our first Christmas Eve in Gardner House in 1930, as I stood with Miss Smith beside this same fireplace and lighted its first fire, that I should ever see my portrait hanging over it. Emotions of pride and humility and joy crowd out the words that I would like to say. For once I am almost speechless. No doubt there have been times —

I hope only a few — when some of you former students would have liked to have had that happen.

My friends here have said many kind things. They have put a heavy coat of shining enamel over all the inadequacies. I hope Saint Peter had a listening ear. Be assured I shall always treasure the memory of this happy occasion.

To the members of the Alumnae Association I am grateful. You have given me a great honor, but there is one honor that we share together — the honor of being graduates of this school of nursing. Of all the titles which I have had in my professional career, there was none that ever surpassed that of being director of this school and nursing service. I am proud, as you must be, to have been part of this great institution which goes from strength to strength in its educational program and in its service to the children of the world.

It amused me when a student nurse at the hospital where I was being cared for recently told me that when she was an affiliating student at the Children's, she got engaged under my portrait. "That's where we used to sit," she said, "and my fiancé used to look at the portrait and say that he thought we were being well chaperoned." I told her to tell him that I never really looked very often.

The new building which housed all clinical services of the Children's and Infants' Hospital was opened in the spring of 1956. Dr. Guy W. Brugler, the administrator at that time, invited me to participate in the transfer of the first patient, Paul Flanagan, to the new building. Parkman D. Howe, President of the Hospital Board, Muriel B. Vesey, Director of the Nursing Service and School, Dr. Brugler and I had our picture taken each with a hand on the head of the bed while pushing it along. Elizabeth Hutchins, a head nurse, was also in the picture, but she did not have a hand in the procedure.

Certainly there were hard and discouraging times, but had I not been happy at the Children's Hospital, I would have accepted one of the alluring offers for positions in graduate and undergraduate collegiate programs and at national headquarters. Of these offers I received, I shall refer to only one: I was asked to succeed Isabel M. Stewart as Director of the Division of Nursing Education at Teachers College, Columbia University, in 1945. I pondered long and seriously about it, and had I been younger (I was then nearly 59 years old), would have accepted. I told Dean Russell that I felt that a tenure of six years to an age 65 retirement was too short to accomplish much. He did not agree with me, but I was not persuaded to accept. Some of the correspondence with Isabel Stewart and Dean Russell, as well as a gracious letter encouraging me to accept the appointment from Mrs. Winters Mead, the daughter of Helen Hartley Jenkins and a trustee of Teachers College (I had worked on some committee with her), are included in my papers in the Nursing Archive, Mugar Library.[6] One or two letters between Dean Russell and me are missing. After my interview with Dean Russell, I walked along Amsterdam Avenue for miles praying that I would make a right decision. I think I did. After I wrote Dean Russell of my decision, both he and Isabel Stewart asked me to reconsider. I did not change my decision, but the invitation to succeed such great leaders as Mary Adelaire Nutting and Isabel Maitland Stewart was the great honor of my professional career.

References

1. *Bulletin of the Alumnae Association of The Children's Hospital School of Nursing, Boston.* Vol. XVII. August, 1937.
2. Goostray, Stella. *Fifty Years, A History of the School of Nursing, Children's Hospital, Boston.* Alumnae Association. 1941.
3. Correspondence with New York State Board.
4. Letter, Stella Goostray to J. Wells Farley, September 24, 1945.
5. Letter, Stella Goostray to J. Wells Farley, January 17, 1951.
6. Letters, Dean Russell, Isabel M. Stewart, Mrs. Winters Mead, Stella Goostray. Goostray Collection, Folder 6, Box 1, Nursing Archive, Mugar Library, Boston University.

Chapter Five

SO-CALLED RETIREMENT

THERE was no lack of opportunities for part-time work after I left the Children's.   In the fall, Clara Quereau asked me to make accrediting visits with her, and we made quite a number in New England. In the spring of 1947, we went to Chicago to survey the nursing service of Cook County Hospital.   We had hardly started when I showed symptoms of a rheumatic condition, with high fever, and I returned home to spend most of the next year ill or recuperating. Later, Hazel Goff, Anne Taylor Howard and I worked for several months in New York summarizing the visitors' reports for the Board of Review of the National Accrediting Committee. One of the projects I enjoyed was preparing the target revision of the *Hospital Nursing Service Manual,* the section on costs of which was done by Blanche Pfefferkorn. The sponsoring committee had representatives of five organizations, but the active participants were the representatives of the National League of Nursing Education and the American Hospital Association.   The representatives fired their shots at two target revisions, and then I wrote the *Manual* as it appeared in 1950.[1]

I continued to serve on some national committees, but I soon became more involved in the local situation. I had always felt obligated to serve on committees of the state association and state and local league.   Now I got into more time-consuming involvements.   I became the chairman of the Nursing Council of Greater Boston and served from 1947 to 1950. During this term, the Council was in the midst of deliberations on the establishment of the United Community Services. The Nursing Council became a part of UCS, and I had the honor of being one of the incorporators. Although no longer chairman of the Nursing Council when the organizational structure was set up, I was asked in my own right as a citizen to become a member of the first Board of Directors of UCS.

Another interesting bit of study was at the Boston City Hospital, on invitation of Dr. William McNary, the administrator, when plans were being made for new classrooms and a proposed nurses' residence. Dr. McNary had tried to persuade me, aided and abetted by Dr. William Castle and Dr. Soma Weiss of the Harvard Medical School, to become the director of the nursing service and school of nursing in the mid-'thirties. I told Dr. McNary there was "too much political interference." Dr. McNary termed it "political annoyance." I also told him that the salary offered was not commensurate with the job, and he asked me to suggest what it should be. I believe my suggestion was $4000 with full maintenance. He returned the next day to say he had been to see the mayor, and the salary was fixed at that amount. I did not take the job, but at least I had done something for the next director of nursing.

With regard to the new building at Boston City, I found that the space assigned by the architects for one new classroom was near the one cafeteria, and all employees would have to pass its door. Imagine a teacher having to contend with the tread of hundreds of feet, the talk and the raucous laughter if she were teaching a class at the noon hour. When we went to the old nurses' residence, I noted that the closets were too shallow to accommodate a clotheshanger. When I commented on that fact, a woman doctor trustee who had barged in on the visit said, "They are lucky to have any closet." If that was typical of her attitude in other things about the hospital, what an enlightened trustee she was!

Before I leave these more personal memoirs, I want here to include my association with the establishment of a department of nursing education which led to a university school of nursing, and also to an associate degree program in nursing. But for background I must go back in history to my contacts with Dean Davis of Boston University School of Education.

My experience with the Committee on the Grading of Nursing Schools had stimulated me to write my thesis for the master's degree in education at Boston University on accreditation in relation to schools of nursing. I applied to Professor Davis at Boston University School of Education for permission to enter his seminar, but he seemed not particularly interested when I told him I was a nurse. The students in his seminar were mainly superintendents of schools and principals of high schools, and he told me that there were no vacancies in the seminar. We chatted for a while about his participation in a project for teaching student nurses in Grand Rapids Junior College during World War I. He seemed greatly pleased when he found I knew about the project. In his *Saga of a Schoolmaster*, Dr. Davis refers to this program as leading to a central school.[2] I can find no evidence of this permanent result. I believe the project was in effect the purchase of service by three local training schools for teaching in the sciences when teachers were not available for the individual schools.[3]

I left Dr. Davis' office with no assurance that I would be in the seminar. However, two days later I got a postcard saying I would be admitted. The thesis was written on *The Significance of Accreditation for Nursing Schools*.

Later I came into close association with Dr. Davis, who had become the Dean of the School of Education, when a committee from the Massachusetts League of Nursing Education, of which I was a member, at his request explored with him and his associates the possibility of establishing a Division of Nursing Education in Boston University School of Education. My prediction, expressed to Dean Davis when I was a member of his seminar, that increasing numbers of nurses who wanted better preparation for teaching would be enrolling in the School of Education, proved true. By 1938 there was a sufficient number of them to arouse the Dean's interest. The history of that project is in the files of the Boston University School of Nursing.

The program began in the fall of 1938 when a lecture course on

"Trends in Nursing Education" was offered. There was an encouraging response from the nurses, and over two hundred enrolled. Annie W. Goodrich, I believe, gave the opening lecture, and speakers came from many areas to participate. I have forgotten now what my particular topic was. In the spring of 1939, the Department offered a course on "Orientation to Nursing Education" with me as the scheduled teacher. I began the course, but a bout of pneumonia interfered, and Laura R. Logan, who was then at the Boston City Hospital, completed it. I did teach the course again in 1941-1942.

During the period when the nursing program was a Division of Nursing Education in the School of Education, there was an Advisory Committee from the League, and as one might surmise, there were times when problems arose, although we had drawn up guidelines for the Division which were acceptable to Boston University and to our committee. I was a member of the Advisory Committee during its life, and more than once Dean Davis consulted me about some of the snags when he did not want to bring them before the whole Advisory Committee.

It was a historic day for all concerned with the development of nursing education in Boston when the Division became an autonomous School of Nursing, with Martha Ruth Smith, who had headed the Division, as Dean. Thus it was that a nurse educator became the first woman academic dean in the history of Boston University. In 1946-1947, in the new University School of Nursing, I taught a course on "Administration in Schools of Nursing."

In the latter part of 1946, I was asked by the Dean to make a study of the basic programs in collegiate schools of nursing. My report is dated January 15, 1947, and is in the Mugar Nursing Archive. I found that only sixteen schools of nursing held membership in the Association of Collegiate Schools of Nursing based on their undergraduate program. There were eight schools which held associate membership. This report covered fifteen of those which had full membership, and seven of those with associate membership.

Sometime early in the 'fifties there was considerable feeling among students that there was overlapping in the nursing courses, and Dean

Smith asked me to make a study of their content. During part of the time when I made the study, I think Dean Smith was away, since I seem to remember Professor Marie Farrell presiding at faculty meetings which I attended. All members of the faculty except one readily turned over to me the outlines of their courses, and she finally capitulated.

When Boston University in 1967 conferred on me the honorary degree of Doctor of Science, I took occasion in my response to Dr. Case's introduction at the luncheon following the commencement exercises to recall the beginning of nursing education at Boston University: "I was present at the borning of nursing education at Boston University. The borning-room, as it were, was a small corner of the School of Education on Exeter Street. The late Dean Davis and the present Dean of Sargent College, George Makechnie, were the godfathers, and the nurses, of which I was one, were the godmothers."[4] I regarded the awarding of that degree as a recognition of the importance of nursing in the social order of today. And naturally, there was personal pride in having contributed to my profession something which was deemed to have had value in helping to raise the standards of nursing education, that nurses may be more adequately prepared for the complex responsibilities they face in meeting the nursing and health needs of all people, in a society that has new goals for health services.

An Associate Degree Demonstration Project

The other collegiate venture in which I had a part was the establishment of the Associate Degree Program in Newton Junior College. The complete record of that demonstration project is included in the papers of the Greater Boston Nursing Council in the Nursing Archive, Mugar Library, but I should like to refer to one or two aspects of it.

When the United Community Services of Metropolitan Boston, Health, Hospitals, and Medical Care Division, received a grant from the United States Public Health Service for a regional health project in 1956, Alfred L. Frechette, M.D., the Director of that Division, was concerned that there should be some participation by the nursing profession.[5]

In the spring and summer of 1956, the Greater Boston Nursing Council went into action by having a series of three informal meetings to explore the possibility of having a regional nursing education program somewhere in the Boston area. Although there had been many two-year associate degree programs throughout the United States, there was not one in New England. However, Lasell Junior College had a three-year program, the three-year length prescribed by the Approving Authority for Schools of Nursing in Massachusetts. Eventually, we came up with plans for a school at which the clinical teaching and practice would be given in five community hospitals in the Greater Boston area: Arlington, Waltham, Woburn, Concord and Winchester. None of these hospitals at that time had a school of nursing.

The Nursing Council appointed an Advisory Committee to the Council for the Regional Nursing School Program with its members representing a very wide variety of community viewpoints, including a trustee of a hospital, an administrator of a hospital, directors of hospital and collegiate schools of nursing, a social anthropologist, a housewife, instructors in schools of nursing, and the administrator of the Community Junior College of Newton, Massachusetts. I was appointed Chairman.

When it was decided that we would try to establish an associate degree program, no definite selection had been made of a junior college. They were few and far between in this area, but Newton Junior College was finally selected, provided that the authorities would agree to it. Then there followed a series of meetings with the school committee of Newton and the superintendent of the Newton Schools, whom we found to be very helpful. The Trustees of the five community hospitals selected gave warm support. Our difficulty came with the Approving Authority for Schools of Nursing and Schools of Practical Nursing, and did we have a hassle! A petition was drawn up by the Nursing Council asking for approval of the nursing school for a six-year demonstration project and submitted to the Massachusetts Approving Authority. Permission for this demonstration did not involve any change in the law but was only a matter of a Board regulation. In spite of all the approvals and backings which the Advisory Committee had, the opposition led by a hospital trustee on the Approving Authority was very vigorous.

Eventually the approval was granted, and the school began its six-year demonstration program in 1959. The money for the support of the school was raised by the Greater Boston Nursing Council and was largely the gift of local and national foundations. Success in bringing this project to fruition would not have been achieved without the leadership of Dorothy Hayward, Nursing Associate, United Community Services of Greater Boston, who not only did much of the planning for the program, but also was responsible for obtaining the financial support.

The Newton Junior College Associate Degree Program in Nursing, the first two-year associate degree program in New England and the first in the United States on a regional basis, concluded its demonstration in 1965. The associate degree program still goes on, but it is no longer a regional program. There are a variety of reasons for the discontinuance of a regional program including changes in the administration of the cooperating hospitals, because the city of Newton, which then became financially responsible for the support of the program, could hardly be expected to support a program of that nature. Our project was a demonstration, and those of us who were closely concerned with it believed that a regional program had excellent possibilities.

One can hardly separate what are personal memoirs from those concerned with participation in local and national movements, and with this observation I shall conclude the first section of these reminiscences.

References

1. *Manual of Hospital Nursing Services.* NLNE and AHA. 1950. Preface.
2. Davis, Jesse B. *Saga of a Schoolmaster.* Boston University Press, Boston. 1956, p. 165.
3. *Ibid.* pp. 264-265.
4. Goostray, Stella. Remarks at luncheon following conferring of degree. May, 1967.
5. United Community Services of Metropolitan Boston. *Health, Hospital and Medical Care Divisions Report.* June 1, 1956 — January 31, 1958.

Chapter Six

INTRODUCTION TO THE NATIONAL SCENE

THIS chapter will reminisce about related and unrelated happenings and situations in the late 'twenties, in the 'thirties, or beyond, with no attempt at chronological order. There are meanderings and flashbacks, but it may help to give background to other events of historic significance which will be discussed in a series of separate chapters.

The three major nursing organizations at the beginning of the second quarter of this century were the American Nurses' Association, the National League of Nursing Education, and the National Organization for Public Health Nursing. The president of each organization served as an ex-officio member on the board of directors of the other two. This tradition had gone on for years and continued until the middle thirties when Clara D. Noyes, Director of the American Red Cross Nursing Service (a true Connecticut Yankee, well versed in parliamentary procedures and the intricacies of corporation regulations) announced at an ANA Convention that it was illegal for the ANA to have ex-officio members on its board. The practice was discontinued by the ANA, but the NLNE continued to have as ex-officio members the president of the ANA and the editor of the *American Journal of Nursing*.

The boards of directors of the three organizations met each year in January, and usually when there was a joint convention, which used to occur every two years. Joint committees were appointed at these meetings as well as joint committees of the three boards to work with other organizations. A fine distinction was made between the two. These latter committees were never considered joint committees but joint committee with such and such organization, and there was strict adherence to this procedure. I well remember the discussion when we were forming a joint committee with the National Association of Colored Graduate Nurses (1940). Since I was a member of the first committee, representing the NLNE, it was suggested we call it a "Joint Committee of AHA, NLNE, NOPHN and NACGN," for we were working quite closely with the last organization then. But the suggestion was not accepted by the Joint Board. We still had sticklers for the old order. The Joint Board worked together amicably in the interest of the common good, but we each had our vested interests. The membership of each organization with its officers and staff was primarily concerned with finding ways and means to achieve the purposes of the segment of nursing in which it was especially interested.

My first appointment to a national office was as a member of the Board of Directors of the *American Journal of Nursing* in 1925, being elected to that office by the ANA board. The *Journal* Board elected its own officers. Later I became the secretary of the Board of Directors and then served as its president from 1930 to 1937. The years from the latter part of the 'twenties covered a time of great changes in the business administration and editorial policies of a journal becoming worthy of a growing and progressive profession. Mary Roberts was made a co-editor with Katharine De Witt when she began her work with the Journal. Miss De Witt had been the long-time co-worker of Sophia Palmer and had acted as editor after her death. No organization ever had a more devoted and self-sacrificing worker than Katharine De Witt.

The national nursing organizations had established headquarters in New York, and in November, 1923, an editorial office for Miss Roberts was provided, but the main office of the *Journal* remained in Rochester. I attended several Board meetings at those cramped and crowded headquarters in Rochester. It soon became evident that Mary

Roberts wanted the main office in New York. It was natural, too, that she should be dissatisfied with co-editor status, because we were moving into new times, and she and Miss De Witt did not have the same concept of a professional journal. Making a great sacrifice, Miss De Witt went to New York when the office was moved there in 1928 and accepted the position of business manager. The 'thirties marked the beginning of a new life for the *American Journal of Nursing*. It was on its way to becoming a truly professional magazine and so began to attract more advertisers. As anyone who has been connected with a publication such as this knows, it is the revenue from advertising which really supports the magazine. I well remember the year we declared a dividend in the amount of $8,000, payable to the only stockholder, the American Nurses' Association. It was the first dividend ever declared by the company, I believe. There are other sources for the history of the *American Journal of Nursing*, but I should like to comment on one change in policy which took place in the 'thirties.

The *American Journal of Nursing* was recognized not only as the official organ of the ANA, but also of the NLNE. There had been a more or less gentlemen's agreement, or shall we say ladies' agreement, that the *Journal* would not publish material on public health nursing because the NOPHN had its own journal, *Public Health Nursing*. Miss Roberts felt that a professional journal should meet the needs of all groups, and that it should be publishing general material on public health nursing. It was voted to do so. The secretary, Julia Stimson, was instructed to write and convey this information to the Board. Well, that change in policy certainly got me into a somewhat embarrassing situation, because I was wearing more than one hat.

I was a member of the NOPHN's committee on the magazine, as a representative of either the ANA or NLNE. The evening of the same day that we had the *Journal* meeting at which the change in policy was made, there was a meeting of the NOPHN mazagine committee. Our committee meetings were usually held during the week of the Joint Board meetings in New York each January. As the discussion at the meeting progressed, I was getting more and more nervous, because I knew of the *Journal* Board's action. But since I was not serving on the NOPHN committee as a representative of the *Journal*, and had not been authorized by the *Journal* to convey any message to that committee, I made no comment when certain matters came up. But I did pass a note to the General Director of the NOPHN, Dorothy Deming, asking her if she had received the communication and was she going to divulge its contents to the committee. She whispered back to me, since I was sitting next to her, that she had the communication, but was not bringing it up. So, I began to feel a little more content.

When at the Joint Board meeting the next morning Julia Stimson, as secretary of the *Journal* board, mentioned the change in policy, you can imagine the consternation of the members of the NOPHN magazine committee. They were up in arms and, of course, were directing all their wrath toward me. They talked to Mrs. Anne Hansen, who was on the *Journal* board and a former president of the NOPHN, and to Emilie Sargent. They came to me in high gear, but I told them that I was not on that committee as a representative of the *Journal*, that the executive director had the letter from the *Journal* board, and that the announcement should have come from her if the subject was to be brought up. They saw the point, but the matter was not straightened out soon enough for me to escape a tongue-lashing from a volatile member of the committee. She has probably forgotten it long since, and I recall it here only to show how misunderstandings occur and the danger inherent in wearing more than one hat!

In 1928, I was elected secretary of the NLNE, and from that vantage point I could view national events. Quite a number of newspaper clippings are in my file relating to the Milwaukee convention in 1930, a year that begins a decade in which activities were initiated that indicated definite progress in the maturing of a profession.

The White House Conference on Child Care

President Hoover had called a White House Conference on Child Health and Protection to meet in the spring of 1930. One of the subcommittees of the Medical Committee was that on nursing, of which Lillian Clayton was chairman. I was a member of the subcommittee, and we met for some time before the conference. On her death, the chairmanship fell to me. This subcommittee concerned itself primarily with the preparation of young women for nursing in pediatrics, but it realized that the preparation could be considered only in connection with nursing education in general. The Committee on the Grading of Nursing Schools, about which more will appear later, had begun to analyze the reports from the schools of nursing, and the need for reformation in our schools was clearly indicated. Earlier in its studies, the Grading Committee had pointed out that there was an oversupply of poorly prepared and an undersupply of well-prepared nurses, and that the exploitation of student nurses for cheap nursing labor in hospitals which were in no position to offer an adequate nursing education either in theory or in clinical experience was the underlying cause of poor nursing service in all branches. Schools of nursing in many instances were basing experience for their student nurses on the daily needs of the hospital, without consideration of their future service to the community. In 1927, in three-quarters of the hospitals which had schools of nursing there were no general staff nurses. Many of the causes of dissatisfaction with private duty nurses could be traced back to the deficiency in personal qualifications and general education of young women entering schools of nursing. In no field was the need greater for well-prepared nurses than in pediatric nursing.

The Subcommittee on Nursing of the White House Conference concurred in these conclusions and also endorsed the two principles which the Committee on Grading had gone on record as upholding. These appeared in May Ayres Burgess' *Nurses, Patients and Pocket Books*:

1) No hospital should be expected to bear the cost of nursing education out of funds collected for the care of the sick. The education of nurses is as much a public responsibility as is the education of physicians, public school teachers, librarians, ministers, lawyers, and other students planning to engage in professional public serv-

ice, and the cost of such education should come, not out of the hospital budget, but from private or public funds.

2) The fact that a hospital is faced with serious financial difficulties should have no bearing upon whether or not it will conduct a school of nursing. The need of a hospital for cheap labor should not be considered a legitimate argument for maintaining such a school. The decision as to whether or not a school of nursing should be conducted in co-operation with a given hospital should be based solely upon the kinds and amounts of educational experience which that hospital is prepared to offer.

The Subcommittee on Nursing made recommendations that every effort be made to reduce the supply of poorly trained nurses going out into the community. It also pointed out that in the teaching of pediatric nursing there had been little emphasis on the normal child. Two of the outcomes of that report were a committee in the League charged with studying the education of nurses in the care of the child, and the inclusion of a unit on child growth and development in the Curriculum Guide as part of the course in pediatric nursing. As is usually the case in the formulation of the report of a committee, most of the work falls on the full-time secretary, and sometimes little credit is given to her for the content or the quality of writing. I should like to acknowledge the superb contribution made by Hortense Hilbert.

A New Relationship and a New Department

At a meeting of the Board of Directors of the League in January 1932, a report of its Committee on Functions recommended that "in order to bring about close relationship between the NLNE and the ANA, the ANA be requested to consider the possibility of making the NLNE its Department of Education," and that the Executive Secretary of the NLNE, when functioning in relation to the ANA would function as Educational Secretary of the ANA. This would give her a recognized place at ANA staff and other conferences bearing on educational problems and policies.[1] There was to be no change in the organization and autonomy of the NLNE. No plan was suggested for financial adjustments, but it was indicated that this could wait until the new cooperative relationship had been tried. The ANA voted favorably on the proposal, as did the League at its Convention in April 1932.

The ANA had always accepted the NLNE as its educational advisor, and only the year before the ANA Board advised its legislative section that its activities should be restricted to legislative matters and that questions of school inspection should be left to the NLNE. The official recognition that the NLNE was the Department of Education of the ANA made it possible for the NLNE to aid state boards of nurse examiners which had a direct relationship to the ANA.

I cannot find that we reached any arrangement about finances. The ANA was sympathetic to requests from the League; sometimes we got what we asked for and at other times not. There was no commitment as to whether payments would be made at regular times or in what amounts. Even as late as the early 'forties, the irregular gifts continued, for I found a letter, which I as president of the League wrote to Julia Stimson as president of the ANA, sounding out the ANA as to whether a regular contribution could be made to its Education Department.[2] But regular or not, the contributions continued to be made by the ANA to its Educational Department.

The NLNE was always poor. It worked on the proverbial shoestring. The will and the potential to launch new projects were there, but the money was lacking. I can remember when the expenses of officers only were guaranteed for the board meetings called during a convention. When these were paid, the treasurer, after determining how much money was left in the treasury, announced the percentage of expenses Board members could receive. Whenever someone got a brilliant idea for venturing out on new paths, the first question was, "Where are we going to get the money?" And the question was not always posed by the thrifty New Englanders. We had a watchful treasurer and finance committee! There were great needs, but at that time there were no federal funds or foundation grants to help supply them.

There is an interesting recommendation in the minutes of the NLNE Board in April, 1934, to the effect that, "If finances warrant it, the executive secretary and the director of studies be paid a bonus at the end of the year to cover the reduction in their salaries for the year."[3] At the January meeting in 1937, it was voted that the salaries of the executive secretary and the director of studies be increased to $4,320 per annum beginning July 1.[4] And this for living in New York City!

Faced with new responsibilities and needs and with a great desire to supply education materials so badly needed to help schools adjust their programs during the Second World War, the NLNE, in the early 'forties engaged a professional firm of fund-raisers. One of the first questions asked by them was how much financial support was given to the League by the profession as a whole. The campaign for funds was not as successful as we had hoped it would be, but it did help to meet the cost of producing and printing educational materials.

The year 1932 also was notable for progress, because in that year the NLNE established its Department of Studies, with Blanche Pfefferkorn as its director. She was a graduate of The Johns Hopkins School of Nursing and a former executive director of NLNE who served for a period of four years, 1924-1928, leaving for further study. While at Teachers College, she participated in the survey of the Lincoln School of Nursing, a project sponsored by the College. She also made notable studies at Bellevue Hospital. Miss Pfefferkorn's chief interests were in clinical nursing administration and patient care. With her stop watch in her hand, she went from one clinical unit to another timing nursing procedures, but she also observed the techniques of the procedures. Her observations moved her to write a classic paper, "Pray, Let Us Wash Our Hands."[5] She became interested in cost analysis, and with Dr. Charles A. Rovetta, of the University of Chicago, wrote *Administrative Cost Analysis for Nursing Service and Nursing Education,* a project sponsored by the NLNE and the American Hospital Association. The Department of Studies proved its worth to the League and to many other organizations during World War II, and in my opinion it was a potent factor in promoting cooperative relationships with the AHA and other organizations.

In the ANA, things were not going quite so peacefully. Elnora Thompson of Portland, Oregon had been elected president of the ANA at the Milwaukee Convention. During her terms of office, she had to deal with many difficult situations in relation to headquarters, and it ultimately ended in the resignation of Janet Geister, the executive director. A lot of feeling was created for and against the decision, for Janet Geister had a large following among private duty nurses. There was quite an emotional response and bitter feelings were engendered. My memory is not sufficiently clear to discuss what happened, but Miss Clayton had suggested to me that all was not well at headquarters.

Janet Geister in many ways was a very capable person, and she was almost like a child in other ways. She had a way of pulling something out of her pocket and giving it to you, as for example, at one time she pulled a rabbit's foot out of her pocket and gave it to me saying, "I give these to my friends." I had that rabbit's foot for many years. She could write well and edited *The Trained Nurse* for some time. I am sure that she was concerned with the welfare of nurses and the quality of service they gave, and whatever happened one must remember that she made valuable contributions to nursing. Her papers, at least in part, are now on deposit in the Nursing Archive, Mugar Library, Boston University, and they reveal many facets of her personality and the various projects in which she was involved.

When I addressed a state association in 1935 on "What Lies Ahead for the Nursing Profession,"[6] I stated that "it did not take any gift of prophecy" (although Mary Roberts very generously referred to that paper as "prophetic"[7]) for me to say that if nursing were to advance to new levels of effectiveness in meeting the needs of the new social order that had begun, four changes must be made. These were to advance nursing education in accord with sound educational practices; to develop professional solidarity that would manifest itself in a common endeavor to understand the problems of the whole profession and to participate actively in their solution; to establish basic economic security for all nurses; to bring the consumer of nursing services more actively into the profession's thinking and planning both for education and service. Some of the chapters which follow will discuss events of historic significance through which the profession determined its direction.

Economic Insecurity

I shall refer only briefly to the question of basic economic security, an ongoing problem now as then. Immediately following World War I there was tension, unrest, and economic recession. Surface prosperity returned about 1922, and then we were in the mad decade of the 'twenties with not only one car in every garage, but two and three chickens in every pot. We were at the peak of the number of schools of nursing — over two thousand, many of them in proprietary hospitals where they provided the owners with cheap nursing service.

The economic depression of the early 'thirties came as a tornado after the gay whirrings of the lavish 'twenties. Grading Committee reports and other studies showed that nurses were hard-hit. People did not have money to employ private duty nurses. Hospitals at that time were not employing many "general duty nurses," a classification used in that day. Some nurses were unemployed because of their inadequate preparation in nursing education.

In the memorandum which the League sent to the ANA when it requested the latter to consider an arrangement by which the NLNE became the Department of Education, it included this statement: "Studies of unemployment and the studies of the Grading Committee give factual basis for the belief that the condition of unemployment is rooted in the economic unsoundness of our schools."[8]

It was not unusual to find nurses during the economic depression working for their room and board. Salaries were cut in hospitals, and it always annoyed me that before the percentage cuts were made a charge was added for room and board. This had never happened when increases were given. The percentage increase was made on the basis of cash salary only. The unemployment of the 'thirties did not disappear until World War II called nurses for military service. When the Social Security Act was passed by Congress in 1935, nurses and other hospital workers were not included in old-age security. Much opposition came from the hospitals whose argument was that hospitals were charitable institutions and could not use their funds for the benefit of their employees. However, the hospital association later changed its tune, and nurses and other hospital workers became eligible for old-age security. Certainly hospitals have long since learned that pensions and the other fringe benefits which go with jobs in other fields are an important factor in stabilizing their staffs.

It seemed to me at first somewhat strange and a little hard to accept as a professional person that state nurses' associations were acting as bargaining agents whenever difficulty arose about salaries and other conditions of work. I had hoped employing agencies would see the light, but many of them did not and have not, and nurses must have economic stability as do other workers. Our wishful thinking has to be replaced with realistic action when conditions warrant it.

It may not be amiss to note that the League, at its annual convention in New York in 1935, celebrated the seventy-fifth anniversary of the founding of the Nightingale School by holding a public meeting in Carnegie Hall. Although Miss Nutting was not able to attend, she sent a greeting and paid tribute to the quality of mind of Florence Nightingale that made her never fall back upon tradition and precedent for guidance. "No old way was the right way unless it met with the approval of her reason and intelligence."

Carrie M. Hall gave some of us a lesson in decorum for public meetings when we came down from the platform. She said, "You girls will have to learn that when you are seated on the stage at a formal meeting, even if you are in long gowns, you must not cross your knees."

Nurses as an organized profession had recognized the challenges for change and were moving into action. The results may be assessed today as indicating standards of value for responsible action in their time and also historical continuity in the maturing of a profession.

References

1. *38th Annual Report.* NLNE. 1932, p. 19.
2. Letter, Stella Goostray to Julia C. Stimson, May 22, 1942.
3. Minutes, NLNE Board of Directors. April, 1934.
4. Minutes, NLNE Board of Directors. January, 1937.
5. Pfefferkorn, Blanche. "Pray, Let Us Wash Our Hands." *American Journal of Nursing.* August, 1932, p. 851.
6. Goostray, Stella. "What Lies Ahead for the Nursing Profession," *American Journal of Nursing.* August, 1935, p. 376. Also reprint.
7. Roberts, Mary M. "Stella Goostray." *American Journal of Nursing.* March, 1958, p. 354.
8. *38th Annual Report.* NLNE. 1932, p. 19.

Chapter Seven

THE PROFESSION WANTS ITS SCHOOLS GRADED

THE phenomenally rapid growth of the training schools, as most of them were called, from 1890 to 1910 created conditions which were far from desirable judged from an educational viewpoint. But nursing was not alone. Medical education in the United States also had its difficulties. There were many proprietary medical schools located in a room or two in the basement of a building in a cheap neighborhood, with a couple of doctors giving the instruction, and, after offering little if any clinical experience, sending out their so-called graduates to practice medicine. And under the existing laws in some states they could do so. There were several schools on Shawmut Avenue in the city of Boston. At this time also there were diploma mills grinding out diplomas in medicine for a price. Much of this condition changed after the study by Dr. Abraham Flexner on medical education in the United States and the publication of his report.

Leaders in nursing education, foremost among whom were Adelaide Nutting and Isabel Stewart, hoped that nursing might have a similar study made of its educational system by an independent group. The Education Committee made a request to the Carnegie Foundation to make such a study, and it was with great sorrow that Miss Nutting had to report to the convention of the National League of Nursing Education in 1912 that the request had not been granted. But Adelaide Nutting was a persistent woman.

The Rockefeller Foundation in 1919 appointed a committee, of which Miss Nutting was a member, to make the nursing study, and the report of that committee was published in 1923 as *Nursing and Nursing Education in the United States.* The chairman of the committee was Dr. Charles-Edward A. Winslow and the secretary, Josephine Goldmark. Reference to that committee and its findings are available in Roberts' *American Nursing.*[1] Unfortunately, the study was limited in size. This study did not satisfy many of the nursing leaders, who felt that an insufficient number of schools (23) had been included. They pressed for a study which would include all state board accredited schools. "Accredited" was the word commonly used for schools recognized by state boards of examiners, and the lists published at that time had not the same significance as the lists of accredited schools now current.

Even though the study backed by the Rockefeller committee was limited in scope, had the recommendations been accepted and followed by action in the schools, there would have been a far-reaching effect on nursing and nursing education. But in general they were not. However, as a result of that study, the Western Reserve (Frances Payne Bolton School) University School of Nursing and the Yale University School of Nursing were established. The profession immediately began to raise funds for a five-year study of nursing education. About this same time, some members of the medical profession were pressing for a study of the education and employment of nurses in order to evaluate the service which they might expect. The American Medical Association agreed to be represented on the committee, which was being created largely through the efforts of the three national nursing organizations. The Committee on the Grading of Nursing Schools came into being in 1926. Shortly after the Committee was organized, the AMA withdrew without giving any reason for their action. Dr. William Darrach, one of their representatives, who had been chosen chairman of the Committee, was made a member-at-large and continued as chairman throughout the Committee's life. Of the budget of approximately $300,000, nearly one-half came from the personal contribution of individual nurses and the three national nursing organizations. Contributions from some foundations and generous friends of nursing were included in the remainder.

The organizations represented and the members of the Committee made a roster of leaders who could hardly have been more representative of the fields of nursing, hospital administration, public health, medical education, general education, and concerned citizens. For some reason the leading histories of American nursing do not give the names of these leaders. It seems to me that they are worthy of being named, and I do so here. I worked with them and know the calibre of these men and women and the commitment which they made to that study.

Committee on the Grading of Nursing Schools
and Organizations Represented

THE NATIONAL LEAGUE OF NURSING EDUCATION:

Elizabeth C. Burgess, R.N., Associate Professor of Nursing Education, Teachers College, Columbia University, New York City.

Laura R. Logan, R.N., Director, Cook County School of Nursing, Chicago, Ill.

THE AMERICAN NURSES' ASSOCIATION:

Helen Wood, R.N., Newton, Mass.

Susan C. Francis, R.N., Superintendent, The Children's Hospital of Philadelphia, Philadelphia, Pa.

THE NATIONAL ORGANIZATION FOR PUBLIC
HEALTH NURSING:

Katharine Tucker, R.N., General Director, National Organization for Public Health Nursing.

Elizabeth G. Fox, R.N., Executive Director, Visiting Nurse Association, New Haven, Conn.

THE AMERICAN COLLEGE OF SURGEONS:

> Malcolm T. MacEachern, M.D., Associate Director, American College of Surgeons, Chicago. Ill.
>
> Bowman C. Crowell, M.D. (Alternate), Associate Director, American College of Surgeons, Chicago, Ill.

THE AMERICAN HOSPITAL ASSOCIATION:

> Joseph B. Howland, M.D., Superintendent, Peter Bent Brigham Hospital, Boston, Mass.
>
> Ada Belle McCleery, R.N. (Alternate), Superintendent, Evanston Hospital, Evanston, Ill.

THE AMERICAN PUBLIC HEALTH ASSOCIATION:

> Charles-Edward A. Winslow, D.P.H., Professor, Public Health, Yale University, New Haven, Conn.
>
> Haven Emerson, M.D. (Alternate), Professor, Public Health Administration, College of Physicians and Surgeons, Columbia University, New York City.

MEMBERS-AT-LARGE:

> Mrs. Chester C. Bolton (The Hon. Frances Payne Bolton), Lyndhurst, Ohio.
>
> Sister Domitilla, R.N., Director of Nursing Education, St. Mary's School of Nursing, Rochester, Minnesota.
>
> Henry Suzzallo, Ph.D., President, The Carnegie Foundation for the Advancement of Teaching, New York City.
>
> Samuel P. Capen, Ph.D., Chancellor, University of Buffalo, Buffalo, New York.
>
> Edward A. Fitzpatrick, Ph.D., Dean, Graduate School, Marquette University, Milwaukee, Wisconsin.
>
> W. W. Charters, Ph.D., Professor of Education and Director of Bureau of Education Research, The Ohio State University, Columbus, Ohio.
>
> William Darrach, M.D., Dean Emeritus, College of Physicians and Surgeons, Columbia University, New York City.

Winford H. Smith, M.D., Director, The Johns Hopkins Hospital, Baltimore, Maryland.

Nathan B. Van Etten, M.D., General Practitioner, New York City.

The nursing organizations had envisioned the Committee as beginning a study of nursing education which would lead to the actual grading, and in their minds it meant a classification of schools such as excellent, good, bad or indifferent. But the Committee decided that they should adopt a wider purpose, and they expressed it as "the study of ways and means for insuring an ample supply of nursing service of whatever type and quality is needed for adequate care of the patient at a price within his reach." So began what was supposed to be a five year program covering three types of study, to be made in this order:

1.   A study of supply and demand.
2.   Job analysis.
3.   Grading of the nursing schools.

The nursing organizations pressed for the study of the schools, and this was made before the job analysis. The final report came out in 1934, eight years after the study began. My comments will be confined mainly to the third study. The work on the so-called grading of schools did not begin until 1929. However, early in its work the Grading Committee affirmed two principles relating to schools of nursing that are noted in the previous chapter. As soon as the study of the schools began, three national nursing organizations formed a joint Committee on Educational Policies whose purpose was to help the Grading Committee when it began to analyze the returns. They invited me to become educational advisor and to be the liaison between this committee and the Grading Committee. The Grading Committee later made me a consultant. Mary M. Roberts, editor of the *American Jonrnal of Nursing* was the other consultant.

I went to New York on January 1, 1930, after the reports from the schools had been received, these having gone out to the schools during

1929. I worked with Dr. Burgess for a period of seven months, and also continued to make periodic visits to New York when the second grading material was being studied. I saw the individual reports from all schools, and I never would have believed that schools could have been approved by the state boards of nursing examiners with conditions as they were.

Reference to the three sections of the first grading study will indicate the statistical methods used and the type of reports which went to the schools. Part of my job was to write letters to the schools. It was a form letter with special added paragraphs to meet indicated needs. When the Grading Committee gathered its information, there were 1,885 state approved schools of nursing, including approximately thirty collegiate or university schools. However, the Grading Committee sent the forms to all schools in the country which were listed, accredited or not, and so some 2,205 so-called schools were invited to participate (I don't remember the source of the list). Some of these schools were for affiliating students only and were accredited as such by a state board of examiners. But, in that number were also schools which were not accredited by anybody, yet their graduates were going out and practicing. I was rather surprised when I found that these schools had been included in the invitation, because it seemed to me that here was a committee sponsored by professional organizations giving a sort of recognition to them as schools. Of course, there were many correspondence schools in the country which blatantly advertised their wares.

Of the 2,205 schools which received invitations, sixty-six percent or just over 1,450 responded, and as practically 1,400 of these were state-approved schools, this left only approximately fifty to sixty schools which might be state-approved affiliating schools or the non-recognized schools. Most of the state-approved schools which did not participate were very small schools, so that the statistical picture of the upper half of the schools, that is those to be regarded as the better half, would not have been much affected by their omission.

In only half of the schools reporting were at least two-thirds of the students graduates of high schools. Incidentally, the Board of Directors of the American Nurses' Association on May 9, 1918 went on record as believing that the minimum standard of admission to a state-approved school of nursing after January, 1922, should be high school graduation. In the Commonwealth of Massachusetts, it took us until the year of the sixtieth anniversary of the establishment of the first school of nursing within the Commonwealth to get high school graduation as a requisite for admission, and that without defining the type of high school or making any requirements as to the subjects studied.

The average school studied in the first grading had forty-nine students, and there were schools which had three to nine students. In one-fourth of all the approved schools studied there were twenty-two or fewer students. Only half of the schools studied were in hospitals that had a daily average of more than seventy-five patients. A quarter of the schools were in hospitals that had fewer than forty-five patients. There were nine schools in hospitals with a daily average of five to nine patients, sixty-four had ten to nineteen patients, and 109 were in hospitals that had twenty to thirty patients.

We found a few schools calling themselves collegiate schools of nursing whose students had their clinical teaching in hospitals with a daily average of less than seventy-five patients. Smallness in itself may not be too valid a criterion, but smallness associated with the other detrimental factors that we found rather consistently in these small schools made smallness worthy of note.

One of the most appalling variations was that in the amount of time students in the same graduating class spent in the various clinical experiences. It was obvious that service needs superseded educational needs. Far too many students spent a disproportionate time — sometimes a whole year — in the obstetrical service or the operating room. On one of the reports in answer to the question about regularly scheduled classes I found this naive statement: "We do not have regularly scheduled classes because the owners make rounds every day and quiz nurses." Too many hospitals were using students to relieve telephone operators and elevator operators. And we found students who were acting as night supervisors.

The educational background of the faculty left much to be desired, and in many schools some of the students were better educated than their teachers. Although the reports presented a depressing picture of nursing education, I think they gave a reliable picture of what was characteristic of the schools in this country in the late 'twenties and 'thirties.

I have often thought that if the Grading Committee had sought less information and therefore had sent back to the schools much less complicated material we might have gotten better results than we did. Certainly these educational statistics and the use of technical terms, although they were all fully explained, were to me somewhat of a deterrent in getting people to study them. Each school, of course, received four copies of the report, one for the director of the school, one for the administrator, one for the chairman of the board of trustees and the fourth for the chairman of the school of nursing committee.

The first report was in three sections:
1. Student Body.
2. What Students Learn.
3. Who Controls the Schools.

I made a Special Study of the Nursing School Curriculum, which was printed in Section Two, and a Summary of Suggestions Relative to the Curriculum for Section Three. Both of these were accepted by the Committee and voted to be official parts of the report.

I doubt very much if many other than directors of nursing and some of the administrators really studied them. But there was a salutary effect on nursing that was shown by the improvement two years later when facts were gathered for the second grading. For the second grading, the schools sent in the forms supplied by the Grading Committee each month from January through October, 1932. Seventy-nine percent of accredited schools participated in this study. Non-accredited schools were not invited to participate.

Many schools were closed before the second grading, but this was not entirely due to the Grading Committee reports, for we were still in the midst of the Great Depression. My copies of stenographic reports of the Grading Committee meetings from 1930 to 1934 (perhaps the only ones in existence) are now safely deposited in the Nursing Archive, Mugar Library, Boston University, and anyone making an in-depth study of nursing education in this country should read those minutes.

A Disappointing Decision

It was an exceedingly great disappointment to nurses when the Grading Committee decided that it was not wise at that time to classify the schools as to merit. There was agreement on the part of the Committee that some form of grading should follow with the nursing profession doing its own grading. Chancellor Capen was well known as an outspoken and vehement critic of standardizing agents, and he spoke as though he had felt the heavy hand of a standardizing agency. He expressed his views many times at meetings of the Grading Committee, and his main argument was that an injustice would be done to some schools if they were classified on the basis of their reports to the Grading Committee. Chancellor Capen was exceedingly warm in his praise for the nursing profession in having made possible the study. He characterized it as having a self-sacrificing devotion to a great public cause.

One knows, of course, that a school cannot be evaluated from facts given on a series of educational, statistical charts, no matter how fine they are or how much factual information they give. They certainly do not get at the essence of a school as an educational institution. The quality of the products of a school is one of the best testimonies to the school's value. Judged by that standard, we did have some poor schools!

So what the nurses had hoped would be an actual classification of the schools turned out to be self-surveys of the schools by means of forms furnished to them by the Committee on the Grading of Nursing Schools, and then each school was shown where it stood in various areas by means of graphs. The stenographic report of the meeting of the Grading Committee, May 13, 1931, shows plainly the attitude of the League to the Grading Study's not having been completed in the five years allotted to it. They were disappointed, to put it mildly.

Consideration had been given by some of the collegiate schools to forming an association, and the decision of the Grading Committee not to classify the schools was the real stimulus to the organization of the Association of Collegiate Schools of Nursing in the early 'thirties. The Association set up high standards for admission, and this constituted a form of accrediting for collegiate schools.

With the current discussion (1968) on whether hospitals should operate schools of nursing, I am reminded that the question was raised in the Grading Committee: "Is there a legitimate place for a hospital school?" Said Sister Domitilla: "I don't think we are ready to say." Are we yet ready?

The profession has now spoken out on it, but that does not mean that we have yet won the day.

My association with the Committee on the Grading of Nursing Schools was a very happy and profitable experience. Dr. Darrach was an excellent chairman, and as will be seen by the minutes of the meetings, everyone had a chance to have his or her say. If comments were not forthcoming voluntarily, Dr. Darrach asked point-blank for individual opinions.

There were disagreements but never disagreeable situations. Certainly the nurses on the Committee expressed themselves firmly. When we were discussing weaknesses in schools, there was a desire on the part of the nurses to come out with strong statements about them, and we sometimes were a little dismayed, to say the least, when there was talk about "frowning" on these things. On one occasion Miss Burgess stated that we should come out with a strong statement as to what constitutes a good school, not with a set of lowest permissible qualifications. Miss Burgess always showed an admirable forthrightness and a willingness to take issue on controversial matter.

The Committee met for several days at a time, not only in formal meetings, but at meals. On at least one occasion, we had our meeting at Briar Cliff Manor on the Hudson. It was in the dead of winter, and we almost froze. I remember kidding Katharine Tucker, a public health exponent, about not opening her window at night, but neither did I. We would have frozen stiff. Once when a group of us met in the ladies' room, Mrs. Bolton stood on her hands with her feet against the wall. "I've got to get some exercise," said she. She was a great believer in Yoga and was quoted last year as saying she would not have been in the Congress of the United States at the age of eighty-two if she had not been.

Mrs. Bolton, in the days when I knew her, was a firm supporter of sound nursing education. She had believed so firmly in it that she endowed the school of nursing at Western Reserve University. Later she was the moving spirit in getting funds from the Federal government for nursing education, including the appropriation for the establishment of the Student Cadet Nurse Corps. Accompanying a photograph of Mrs. Bolton in Roberts' *American Nursing* is the statement, "The name of the Honorable Frances Payne Bolton was imperishably associated with nursing before she sponsored the act which provided for the U. S. Cadet Nurse Corps in 1943."[2] During the last few years, Mrs. Bolton seems to have been considerably bothered about the professional organization's stand on nursing education, and she has been quoted as blaming the nursing shortage on the "hierarchy in the nursing profession."[3] Although she may differ with some of our points of view today, we cannot forget that much of the progress in nursing education made possible during the war years was due to her efforts.

Some State Board Standards Needed Attention

The fact that schools with such low standards of education as the Grading Committee reports revealed were approved by state boards of nursing indicated for one thing that appointments to these boards were not made on a very selective basis, to say the least.

[81]

When the Board of Directors of the ANA went on record as believing that high school graduation should be a minimum requirement for entrance into an approved school of nursing after January 1, 1922, the profession was warned by Adda Eldredge, a very astute leader, that it should move slowly, because many of the nursing school faculties could not meet this requirement, and neither could a goodly number of state board members, including the persons definitely appointed to inspect or evaluate the schools.

Many of the appointments to state boards were politically engineered. When I was not reappointed to a second term on a state board, I had been told there had been a little political connivance on the part of a former chairman who had found I was not a "Yes woman" and had been pressing hard for better standards.

When any of us tried to make headway in advancing standards one of our colleagues would say in great disdain, "You League palookas are nuts" or "You League people don't know what you are talking about." I did not know what a "palooka" was, and I don't think she did either, but it sounded like a bad word. I have since learned that Joe Palooka in the funnies was a prizefighter, so perhaps she named us more accurately than she knew.

With the election of the next governor an appointment came. At the annual meeting, one of the physician hospital administrators nominated me as chairman. The other nomination, made by the former chairman, was for the person who always referred to the "League palookas." A secret ballot was taken and I was elected. Shortly thereafter, the secretary of the board, a physician who was also secretary of the medical board, asked me not to serve as chairman. He said he did not want me "to be hurt" because the former chairman in his words "is out to get you." I was not to be intimidated, but served as chairman, was re-elected the next year, and refused to be nominated again because I was serving as president of the NLNE. I remained on the Board for another seven or eight years.

Low standards in the state were not always a matter of law but of Board regulations. Too many times educational progress was halted by members of our own profession who were satisfied with the status quo. Some boards were more concerned about the exact number of days and weeks or number or kinds of scrubs in the operating room than in new ways of making the teaching effective. Schools which were ready for courageous experimentation in teaching methods, in curriculum patterns, in evaluating achievements, and in measuring clinical practice by more adequate methods than by months or days or number of scrubs or deliveries got no quarter when they approached state boards.

One of our best state boards of nurse examiners was in New York State. But in my opinion they were too bogged down by red tape. In order for a nurse at this time to be registered in the State of New York, her school had to be registered, and it was regularly visited by an inspector of New York State. Now all this was good, but, whenever you approached them for a ruling about a matter which you believed should be changed, the nurse members always came back with the answer, "We cannot do anything about it; this is a matter for the Commissioner of Education." Now I doubt that the Commissioner of Education was as concerned with the details as they tried to lead us to believe. In other words, it was my belief that he took the interpretation of the nurses.

In my opinion, the Grading Committee's report did have a salutary effect on state boards, and there were many changes made in the 'thirties in both board regulations and state laws. In some states at that time the best-prepared people, that is, those who were members of faculties of schools of nursing, were not allowed to serve as members of the board.

I note that in my League report for 1932 on the margin of a page I have written in shorthand, "I doubt if much can be done through state boards of nurse examiners which have no definite qualifications set for the office." I record this here only because thirty-six years later I am proud that I can translate the shorthand.

In the memorandum which the NLNE sent to the ANA requesting that consideration be given to making the NLNE its Department of Education, there was this statement: "State boards of nurse examiners are the key to any very general improvement in the schools, but at present there is no machinery set up by means of which the NLNE can aid these boards which have a direct relationship to the ANA."[4] The state board of examiners conferences sponsored jointly by ANA and NLNE proved to be an influential factor in raising standards.

The ANA published a digest of laws pertaining to registration of nurses, and references to that in these years would show how diversified were the regulations. Reciprocity between states was a different matter. Today, every state in the union uses the State Board Test Pool, so that nurses can move from state to state without the difficulties that were apparent thirty years ago. The ANA and the NLNE began jointly to sponsor State Board Conferences after the ANA finally accepted the NLNE as its Department of Education.

References

1. Roberts, Mary M. *American Nursing*. The Macmillan Company, New York. 1954, p. 65.
2. *Ibid*. Plate XI, between pp. 288-289.
3. *American Journal of Nursing*. December, 1966, p. 2605.
4. *38th Annual Report*. NLNE. 1932, p. 19.

Chapter Eight

GUIDELINES TO NURSING EDUCATION

SHORTLY after the study on nursing and nursing education in the United States was made by the committee sponsored by the Rockefeller Foundation, the Education Committee of the NLNE began working on the revision of the *Standard Curriculum, 1917.* I have commented in the pamphlet *Three Score Years and Ten* how the word "standard" was interpreted by many schools and about the advertisements that appeared in the *American Journal of Nursing* for instructors with this qualification "Must be able to teach the Standard Curriculum."[1] Working on the revised curriculum as a member of the Education Committee was the first major national project in which I shared. It was a rich learning experience, as was membership on any committee chaired by Isabel Stewart. But it always meant concentrated work in committee meetings and a stiff stint of homework. This was the first time the committee had the aid of a few experts in fields other than nursing in the preparation of the curriculum. When the committee's work was completed I spent some time in New York working with Miss Stewart on the final editing, a fact recalled to my mind when I was preparing a paper several years ago and saw Blanche Pfefferkorn's comment in her annual report as Executive Secretary of the NLNE.[2]

As soon as the curriculum was ready for publication, if not before, Isabel Stewart had another project launched. As she said, there was not much point in preparing a curriculum without having a properly prepared faculty. So we were off again on a study of the duties, qualifications, and preparation of the faculty with Effie Taylor as chairman of the subcommittee on administrators, Mary Marvin on supervisors and head nurses, and myself on instructors. Isabel Stewart was not always an easy person to work with, especially if one were the chairman of a subcommittee and the job included writing. Isabel Stewart wanted it written her way. At one stage Effie Taylor and I "got our backs up" and determined to tell Isabel off, which we did. Effie and I have often laughed about it. Isabel took her chiding like a lamb, and we were left free to do our jobs.

For the study on instructors, thirty instructors kept clock diaries, and from these we made a check-list of 250 items. There was also a questionnaire to determine the educational and vocational backgrounds, the salaries, and the satisfaction and difficulties that went with the job. A list of forty-eight traits was prepared and sent to superintendents of nurses, and we asked the superintendents to rank the traits in the order of their importance and suggest the degree to which the specific instructor should have it. On the returns, humor ranked lowest on the list. Not in my ranking! The other chairmen used similar methods. In the spring of 1927 I commuted from Philadelphia on Saturdays to take several courses at Teachers College, and I know that many of the students were assigned parts to play in those studies.

Isabel Stewart was also interested in the functional analysis studies of the activities of various professions made by Dr. W. W. Charters of the University of Chicago and later of Ohio State University, and she and other members of the Education Committee made some functional analyses of nurses' activities. Dr. Charters was on the Committee on the Grading of Nursing Schools, and one of its studies was an *Activity Analysis of Nursing* by Johns and Pfefferkorn. The authors acknowledged the help given them in the preliminary studies made by Isabel Stewart.

The Education Committee of the NLNE eagerly awaited the final report of the Committee on the Grading of Schools of Nursing in order that it might begin the preparations for the revision of the 1927 Curriculum. The Education Committee began planning its work in 1933 when the reports of the findings of the first two studies on the schools were available and before the final report was published.

Nursing as a social institution was having new demands made upon it which challenged the scope of the curriculum and the validity of our methods. By 1935 the committee now known as the Curriculum Committee had begun its revision of the curriculum. It made a new approach to the preparation of a curriculum. It was the most ambitious and far-reaching program in the League's forty-five-year history. It also affirmed a new philosophy for nursing education.

The Central Committee agreed that the first step in the preparation for curriculum revision was a statement of the aim of the curriculum in order that we might see the end toward which we were moving. We agreed this aim should be in alignment with the aims of general education, which at that time emphasized (1) that all students must be prepared for a social life which was dynamic and which promised to show even greater changes than in the past; (2) consideration of individual differences and development of the student as a person, the emphasis being upon the person rather than the job; (3) the development of methods of teaching designed to arouse within the student a spirit of inquiry and an attitude of mind which led him to solve his own problems.[3]

There was concerted effort to have every member of the League study the proposed program, and the ground was well prepared by a series of articles in the *American Journal of Nursing.* Literally hundreds of League members were involved in that study in addition to the staff at Teachers College and the Central Committee. It was a thrilling example of the widening periphery of participation in our educational projects. Consultants from the fields of general education, medical education, hospital administration, library science, social service, and nutrition gave liberally of time and talent. And faculty members of schools who participated acquired a liberal education in principles of curriculum construction and adjustment.

Although the median school presented a depressing picture of an educational institution, a sufficient number of schools were exceeding the recommendations of the 1927 Curriculum to encourage the Curriculum Committee to increase considerably the hours of recommended instruction. It should be remembered that the League's recommended curricula were intended for those schools which were concerned with giving a sound nursing education as it was envisioned in those days. They were designed as guides to schools, and were never intended to be regarded as legally imposed curricula.

Much of the trouble of the world, as we know, comes from people going off half-cocked about something on which they have little correct information. We had hardly gotten started when it was evident there was a good deal of misconception on the part of some people as to what the League was recommending in the new curriculum. Judging from some of the echoes, one might think we had set off a blast of dynamite without regard for the safety of those in the immediate vicinity. What was mistaken for the blast of dynamite was really a mild clap of thunder. We were not starting a revolution. We proposed an optimum curriculum which might reasonably be put into effect over a period of years. The *Curriculum Guide* recommended an admission requirement to schools of nursing of one year and preferably two years of general education beyond high school.

The preparation of the *Curriculum Guide* was made possible through a generous gift from Miss Mary Johnston of Cincinnati, Ohio, who had become interested in the project by Elizabeth Pierce, the full-time secretary of the Curriculum Committee. Miss Pierce had just retired as administrator of the Children's Hospital, Cincinnati, and the gift was really made as a tribute to her. Later on, Miss Johnston made other generous gifts to special projects of the League.[4]

The *Curriculum Guide* was the last curriculum published by the League, for it was believed that with the progressive changes in nursing education after World War II the time had arrived when the faculty of the individual school should assume responsibility for curriculum development. The League had published curricula in 1917, 1927, and 1937, and each of them knew the scholarly brain and masterly hand of Isabel Maitland Stewart. In my opinion, Isabel Stewart was the most prolific author of timely and scholarly articles on nursing education and the history of nursing that the profession has had up to this time. Most of the pamphlets issued during World War I were the work of Isabel Stewart. I have heard her tell how Miss Nutting would tell her that the Committee on Nursing needed a pamphlet on such and such a subject, and it would be produced by I. M. S. "hot off the griddle."

Essentials of a Good School of Nursing was prepared under the sponsorship of the Committee on Standards, whose chairman was Nellie X. Hawkinson, and after the Committee had prepared their manuscripts, Laura R. Logan was appointed a full-time worker for a period to edit the manuscript and see it through to publication. Nellie Hawkinson was also the chairman of the special committee which prepared the educational bulletins issued during World War II, to be discussed later.

After the *Curriculum Guide* was published, it was logical that there should be some guidelines offered on the administration of the school. A special committee with Effie J. Taylor as chairman was appointed, and it led to the publication in 1940 of *Fundamentals of Administration for Schools of Nursing*. This study was also made possible through the generosity of Miss Mary Johnston.

Here again, as with the preparation of the *Curriculum Guide,* the NLNE was pointing the way in the maturing of the profession by utilizing the knowledge and skills of other professional workers who were concerned with the same problems in general education. Roy W. Bixler, Ed.D., a specialist in educational administration, was in charge of the study, and Floyd B. O'Rear, an expert in educational administration, and Helen E. Davis, a specialist in social research, were consultants to the Curriculum Committee.

References

1. "Want Advertisements." *American Journal of Nursing.* August, 1924, p. 34.
2. Pfefferkorn, Blanche. "Executive Secretary's Report." *33rd Annual Report.* NLNE. 1927, p. 41.
3. Goostray, Stella. "Installation and Operation of the Curriculum." *42nd Annual Report.* NLNE, 1936, p. 177.
4. *4th Annual Report.* NLNE. 1938, p. 57.

Chapter Nine

THE LEAGUE EMBARKS
ON AN ACCREDITING PROGRAM

IT was not long after the Grading Committee made it evident in 1932 that the schools would not be graded that the NLNE appointed a small committee on accrediting. But no plan was ever submitted. At the convention in San Antonio that year, there was much discussion of standardizing agencies. I became so interested in accreditation in relation to schools of nursing that I wrote my master's thesis at Boston University in 1933 on that subject. That thesis is now in Mugar Library, and I have been told it is probably the first thesis on accreditation in relation to nursing that was written.

The Committee on Grading of Nursing Schools concluded its work in 1934 with the publication of the *Activity Analysis of Nursing* by Ethel Johns and Blanche Pfefferkorn and the final report, *Nursing Schools Today and Tomorrow*. In this report, the League was recognized as the organization best equipped to follow up the Grading Committee's suggested programs. A specific recommendation was that the NLNE create a permanent advisory council in nursing education whose members would represent the groups most closely concerned with nursing education, namely nursing, medicine, public health, hospitals, institutes of higher education, and the public. The NLNE did not accept the recommendation to create such a council, but it began working on ways and means to have an accrediting program — not an altogether new idea in the organization.

At the 1935 convention the Committee on Standards, with Nellie Hawkinson as its chairman, recommended to the Board of Directors "that a committee be appointed to study accrediting systems and plans with the idea that the findings be taken to the Joint Board with the proposal that consideration be given to the establishment of some type of agency for the accreditation of all kinds of programs in nursing education."[1] The Board delegated the Committee to make such a study and report back to the Board in January, 1936. This report, based on the literature of and from conferences with the officers of the existing accrediting agencies in general and medical education, covered the purposes of accrediting, plans of organization, methods of financing, and accrediting procedures. The president of the League, Effie Taylor, called a conference on March 16, 1936, at the Hotel Roosevelt, New York. The conference was attended by Roy J. Deffari, Dean of the Graduate School of Arts and Sciences, Catholic University of America, Edward S. Evenden, Professor of Education, Teachers College, Columbia University; Dr. Nathaniel Faxon, Superintendent, Massachusetts General Hospital; Dr. Claude Munger, Superintendent, Grasslands Hospital, Valhalla, N. Y.; Dr. C. E. A. Winslow, Professor of Public Health, Yale University; George A. Works, Dean of Students and Professor of Education, University of Chicago; and twelve nurses, in addition to Miss Taylor, representing the three national nursing organizations and the Association of Collegiate Schools of Nursing.[2] We sat around a table for the better part of a day as experts in accrediting, hospital administrators and nurses posing questions back and forth. Dr. Munger startled the nurses somewhat when he warned that if the accredited list did not contain ninety-eight percent of the schools then approved by state boards of nursing we were doomed to failure. The consensus of the conference was that the League should establish a list of accredited schools of nursing. Before the conference adjourned President Taylor appointed and charged a small special committee consisting of Nellie X. Hawkinson, chairman, Elizabeth Burgess and Stella Goostray, to present an accrediting plan at the

1936 convention. The convention authorized the appointment of a Standing Committee on Accrediting. Since time was needed to acquaint state boards of nurse examiners and state leagues with the plan, the Committee on Accrediting was not appointed until January, 1937, with Anna D. Wolf as chairman. Every effort was made to have this committee represent a wide geographical area, and to include persons familiar with the problems of state boards, collegiate schools and good hospital schools as well as some who were familiar with the Catholic Sisters' problems. It took us a long time to get going, but at least we were on our way. Clara Quereau was appointed as full-time secretary, effective October 1, 1937.

The first move of the new Committee on Accrediting was to call a conference of consultants in April, with representation from the AHA, ACS (American College of Surgeons), the three national nursing organizations, and three consultants, Dr. Evenden, Dr. Works, and Father Schwittala, the president of the North Central Association. It proved to be a very encouraging and constructive conference.[3]

Fifty-odd schools were selected and invited to be the testing grounds for the new program. Much water flowed under the bridge between 1936 and 1941 when the first accredited list of schools was published. At times that water was somewhat turbulent.

Going back in history somewhat for background, we find that shortly after the first grading report, the Catholic Hospital Association established a Nursing Council on Education, and many of the religious orders which operated hospitals worked through this Council (although in 1933, at the request of some Sisters, the League appointed a Committee of Sisters to study the problems of nursing education in their schools). Some of the farsighted Sisters who were members of the League saw their problems as the common problems of all schools and wished to work through the professional organizations.

In May, 1937, Father Schwittala, on invitation, attended a meeting of the League Board. He was not there, however, as a consultant on the Committee on Accrediting, but as president of the Catholic Hospital Association. He had written to the League Board that the Catholic Hospital Association was committed to a plan for accredita-

tion at the request of a large proportion of the Sisters concerned with
Catholic Schools of Nursing. I am now quoting from the minutes of
the meeting which I wrote as secretary.

> Father Schwittala said it was his desire to bring the Sis-
> ters' organizations and the professional organizations to-
> gether rather than in any way to segregate them. He
> stated that the work had gone forward to the point that
> the Catholic Hospital Association had base lines for the
> accrediting procedures, and a trained group of visitors
> ready. He doubted whether the Sisters' schools would be
> willing to have a double accreditation. In other words,
> he believed that there should be one list.

The League president assured Father Schwittala of the desire of
the Board to understand the problems of the Sisters and that the
Board would give his letter serious and sympathetic consideration.[4]
When he said he believed there should be one list, what he meant was
that the Catholic Hospital Association would accredit their schools and
that the League would put them on its list of League-accredited
schools. After Father Schwittala withdrew from the meeting, Sister
Laurentine, a member of the Board, spoke briefly of the desire on the
part of the Sisters who were members of the League to be affiliated
with the League's accreditation. The Board did not agree to the plan
which Father Schwittala proposed.

Again a question came up in April, 1938 when Sister Olivia asked
whether Catholic ethics would be recognized as a basis for accrediting Catholic schools of nursing. The reply of the Board to Sister Olivia
was as follows: "As expressed in its statement of policy, the Committee
on Accrediting has stated, 'A school of nursing will be judged for ac-
creditment in terms of its stated purposes and upon the basis of the
character and the general excellence of the school as a whole.' In its
interpretation of this policy in relation to schools for nursing con-
trolled by religious groups, the Board of Directors of the NLNE an-
ticipates that the religious philosophy and functions of such a school
will be expressed in its aims. The Committee on Accrediting will
recognize this aim as one of importance to the individual school con-

cerned but in the accreditation of that school, the committee's activity will be concerned with the professional preparation of students."[5] The League anticipated that questions similar to the above might be made by other religious groups which operated schools of nursing, and one can readily see what conflicts might have arisen had we recognized the ethics of one group and not another.

Then there was pressure from the American Hospital Association for more control, and this went on after the first list was published. The schools on that list were from the fifty-odd schools selected by the Committee for accreditation visits, and were the schools which the visitors had deemed worthy of accreditation.

Hardly had the list been released, when the Board of Trustees of the American Hospital Association asked that members of the League Board attend a meeting in Chicago to consider the accrediting program. The Board empowered certain members to attend that meeting. I was president of the League at the time, and, as I recall, we had to leave the post-convention Board meeting in Detroit and go by late train to Chicago. We thought we were meeting with the Board of Trustees of the American Hospital Association, but you cannot imagine our surprise to have present also the Board of Trustees of the Catholic Hospital Association and Sister members of its Council on Education. We had a long and somewhat disturbing meeting because of the demands that were being made on us by this group for a voice in the policy-making plans of the accrediting program. We were equally firm in our stand, and I remember Ada Belle McCleery, who was a trustee of the Hospital Association and my predecessor as secretary of the League, passing me a note which said, "You will have to compromise." As matters developed, it did not seem advisable for us to take any action at that meeting, and immediately following it, the League sent a proposal to the Board of Trustees of the American Hospital Association requesting that it appoint a committee of four to meet with a like number of members of the Board of Directors of the League to consider representation of the American Hospital Association in a policy-making group for the accrediting program.

It was a little surprising shortly thereafter for the president to

[95]

receive from Dr. Basil MacLean a letter which stated that "It is understood that it will be the task of the committtee to develop and have general supervision of the program of accreditation." The letter also stated "that the chairman of the Council on Professional Practice as such is ex-officio member of any subcommittee of that Council." I then wrote Dr. MacLean that I should like clarification of these two matters. I stated that the action at the meeting at which the committee was suggested referred to a policy-forming committee for the direction of the accreditation program. "And that as this was a League activity, naturally, the general supervision of the program would be a function of that organization."

I further pointed out: "As this new committee on accrediting is not a subcommittee of your council but rather a special committee of the League with representatives from a number of organizations, this policy of your organization would not seem applicable. The only ex-officio member provided for in the action taken by the special committee and approved by the League's Board of Directors is the President of the League who naturally is an ex-officio member of all committees."[6] Eventually we did have a policy-forming committee.

Within the committee itself, before the accrediting program began, there were times of great stress, and as a member of the committee itself, I took issue with some of the procedures as did other members of the committee. I thought we were not moving fast enough to get our policies organized and our procedure manual prepared, and that we were following practices that smacked too much of the rigidity of state board regulations. Evidently, the secretary of the committee felt that some of my reactions were personal in nature, since I had raised objections at various times to some of the same rigid procedures of the New York Board's inspectors, and she had been the secretary of that Board.

Now it can be told that at the first meeting of the Board of Directors of the NLNE immediately following the close of the convention at which I was elected president, I was, as it were, called "on the carpet" before the Board. The chairman of the Accrediting Committee, Miss Burgess, at the request of the committee secretary, asked what was to be my position in relation to the policies and procedures of the accrediting program and to the secretary. I was flabbergasted to say the least, inasmuch as the chairman had talked that day with me about it. I thought we had understood each other, but evidently she reported back to the secretary who was not satisfied and who pressed that the matter be brought to the Board.

When I recovered my equilibrium, I asked the vice-president to take the chair while I made my reply, which was that my position and attitude would be as it had been before — that I should not hesitate to voice my opposition to any projects, procedures or policies which I felt were out of place in the program. There was dead silence in the room, and I resumed the chair. That night there was an indignation meeting in Claribel Wheeler's room, she being the secretary of the League. Other members of the Accrediting Committee were there, and it was evident they very much resented the action of the chairman of the Committee. I spent a sleepless night. At a meeting of the Accrediting Committee shortly afterwards, when a matter came up to which I objected, I was mean enough to say, "Why shouldn't this be brought before the Board?" "Oh no! No! No!" said the chairman. "Well," said I, "what was sauce for the goose should be sauce for the gander." And I was not making a pun on my name! When the other members had gone, I remained behind and said to the chairman, "This feud has gone on long enough." We had always been good friends, and I respected her integrity and judgment. And then she said, "I shall never know why I was persuaded to bring that matter to the Board. It has been a matter of great regret to me ever since it happened." I said, "I shall have to continue as before, for that is the only honest thing for me to do, but I shall never again refer in any way to you about what happened at that Board meeting." "Thank you," she said, "and forgive me." That Chairman was Elizabeth Burgess, and I remember her with love and admiration. Well, six years later I retired. When I was asked by the secretary of the Accrediting Committee to make some accreditation visits with her, I agreed, and we had a happy and agreeable time together. So all's well that ends well.

When I made the announcement of that historic event, the publishing of the first list of accredited schools, my comment was, "To me accreditation is one of the greatest strengths we have for the progressive upgrading of our schools of nursing." Now more than a quarter of a century later, I would repeat that statement.[7]

To my knowledge, the accrediting program of the Catholic Hospital Association was never carried out. Some Sisters became visitors for the League's accrediting program in its early stages. The outstanding contributions of the Sisters in the upgrading of nursing education and in stressing a high quality of nursing service, and their work on the boards and committees of our organizations during the past thirty-five years have greatly profited the profession and also helped towards unity within the profession.

References
1. "Secretary's Report." *41st Annual Report.* NLNE. 1935, p. 59.
2. *42nd Annual Report.* NLNE. 1936, p. 60.
3. *43rd Annual Report.* NLNE. 1937, p. 53.
4. Minutes, NLNE Board of Directors, May, 1937, p, 5.
5. Minutes, NLNE Board of Directors. April, 1938, pp. 9, 10.
6. *President's Report.* NLNE Board of Directors. January, 1942.
7. "President's Address." *47th Annual Report.* NLNE, p. 44.

Chapter Ten

THE VENTUROUS CHALLENGE THE CAUTIOUS

DURING the early 'thirties, some schools of nursing had become interested in having prospective candidates for their schools take psychometric tests, the results of which could be used as one of the bases for admission. Most of these schools used the services of the Nursing Testing Division of the Psychological Corporation of New York, of which Edith Potts was Director. But it had long been the hope of Isabel Stewart that the profession would establish and support a testing service of its own. Miss Stewart prepared a section of the 1937 *Curriculum Guide* stressing the importance of these tests.

In 1938, a joint committee of the League, the Association of Collegiate Schools of Nursing, and the Division of Nursing Education, Teachers College was formed to consider the possibility of establishing a testing service. One suggestion was that an effort be made to secure foundation funds and that the committee work through the American Council on Education. No funds were forthcoming, but the League did not relax its efforts.[1]

Miss Stewart gave up the chairmanship of the League's committee on tests when she became involved in the plans for securing Federal funds for nursing education, and Mrs. R. Louise McManus was appointed chairman in 1940. Mrs. McManus had some new ideas for getting started. She attended a League Board meeting in January, 1941, to present a committee report which recommended that the

NLNE authorize the committee on nursing tests to plan for, establish, and operate an NLNE pre-nursing and guidance test service.[2] The recommendation created lively and long discussion. All of the members of the Board expressed their sympathy with the project. We were strong in our belief in its value and had all the good-will in the world to get it started, but the fact was that we were short on dollars, as we usually were.

Finally, the recommendation of the committee was accepted, but it was amended to the effect that the Board authorize the committee to operate on an experimental basis as the NLNE pre-nursing and guidance test service without committing the League to any financial obligation.[3] Authorization was given to the committee to seek funds for underwriting the plan from individuals in states cooperating during the experimental period, and the suggestion was made that before approaching individuals, the committee clear through headquarters.[4]

There were some other aspects of the problem confronting us that do not appear in the minutes of that meeting. One of Mrs. McManus' suggestions was that she obtain a personal loan of fifteen hundred dollars from a member of her family to get the ball rolling. The League president had also received a communication from the president of a large state league protesting the national organization's establishment of this service and intimating that we were competing unfairly with an established service, inasmuch as the Nursing Testing Division of the Psychological Corporation had given the profession good service and had taken a financial risk in establishing it.

Mary Roberts' *American Nursing* comments: "Mrs. McManus proceeded against serious odds reminiscent of those encountered by the founders of the *American Journal of Nursing* almost half a century earlier, to lay sound foundations for one of the profession's most fundamental and useful services . . .Again, the cautious challenged the judgment of those who took bold action."[5]

Mary Roberts' statement is a little inaccurate here. She should have said that the cautious challenged some who wanted to take action without full discussion of the issues involved. When the vote on the recommendations was taken, there were no negative votes, nor did any of the Board refrain from voting. The Department of Measurement and Guidance was established, and it was "one of the profession's most fundamental and useful services," as Mary Roberts said. A good résumé of its first ten years is to be found in the NLNE report for 1952.[6] This was, incidentally, the last report published by that organization.

I admit to being one of the cautious ones, and Isabel Stewart often chided me about it. It was my belief that no organization should establish a new service for which it did not have funds by having the chairman assume personal financial responsibility. Other cautious ones on the Board had a similar point of view. As president, I knew the state of the League coffers. Funds were so low and our needs so great for wartime emergencies, that we had the campaign to raise funds to which I have previously referred.

Then, of course, there was the matter of the letter from the state league taking issue with the national association on establishing the service. We could not ignore the protest, but I did not want to air this matter at the meeting. I therefore asked Miss Burgess to chair a small committee to straighten the matter out. "If this is to be an investigating committee, I will not serve," said the forthright ECB. I assured her that there was no question of investigation, but I felt we had an obligation to pay some attention to the letter, and since she knew Mrs. McManus well, I thought that she could get at what the difficulty was and straighten it out. She did.

From a comment Mrs. McManus made to me at the time, I fear she misunderstood the appointment of the small committee, and I felt bad about that. But let it be recorded here that the first person to greet me as I left the speaker's desk after receiving the R. Louise McManus Award from the Teachers College Alumnae Association, May, 1967, was Louise McManus. Certainly the profession is greatly indebted to Isabel Stewart and to Louise McManus for the sort of faith that removes mountains of caution.

References

1. Minutes, NLNE Board of Directors. April, 1938.
2. Minutes, NLNE Board of Directors, January, 1941, p. 11.

3. *Ibid.* p. 12.

4. *Ibid.* p. 12.

5. Roberts, Mary M. *American Nursing.* The Macmillan Company, New York. 1954, p. 421.

6. Department of Measurement and Guidance. "Bird's Eye View of the First Ten Years of the League's Testing Services." *58th Annual Report.* NLNE. 1952.

Chapter Eleven

THE GREAT DEBATE:
WHO SHALL NURSE FOR HIRE?

ONE subject that was receiving considerable attention during the 'thirties was the number of nursing needs which could be met by other than professionally prepared nurses. If one studies the occupational status of women over the years in city, town or village, one finds evidence that there were always women who earned their living by caring for the sick in their homes, although in this country in 1870 nursing was not included in the seven occupations which accounted for ninety-three percent of girls and women working outside the home.[1] In the appendix to the first edition of *Notes on Nursing* by Florence Nightingale is a table which shows the number of women in Great Britain who earned their living by caring for the sick. Florence Nightingale called them "Nurses by Profession" to differentiate them from those classified as domestic servants, some of whom also did some nursing. These women known as nurses ran the whole gamut from the tippling Sairey Gamps, whom Dickens immortalized, to kindly, compassionate women who through trial and error learned how to care for the sick.

Roberts says, "Thousands of Americans in 1900 had never seen a trained nurse."[2] Perhaps some of the very poor had seen a nurse in training in a hospital, because it was the poor who went to hospitals in that day. The rich had trained nurses care for them in their homes or in the small private hospitals which had been established. But a great number of people knew only the untrained person as the "nurse."

When my brother was born, I was six years old, and a so-called nurse came into our home. She had been there when I was born. She was an English woman, and I disliked her because she would not let me bring my pals into the home as I had always been used to doing. Her favorite comment to me was "Ah, but you're the bad 'un." After the turn of the century, we had a trained nurse during the acute illness of my mother, and then followed the so-called "nurse for convalescence." That trained nurse was on duty twenty-four hours, slept in the room with the patient, and was paid the munificent sum of three dollars a day. My brother was devoted to her, because she made pulled molasses candy for him! For a still later chronic illness came a "trained household attendant." In many states today, untrained women can go into homes to nurse because there is no law that says that all who nurse for hire must be licensed. We have a so-called "mandatory law" in Massachusetts, but it has so many loopholes that it has the effect of a permissive law.

When Annie W. Goodrich was Inspector of Schools in New York and consideration was being given to the licensing of practical nurses, she made a vigorous protest, arguing that until the scope of professional nurses was defined and regulated by law no effort should be made to deal with the status and work of attendants. Later the Rockefeller Committee commented in its report that the subsidiary workers were with us whether we liked it or not, and that they should be trained and licensed.

The growth and development of the licensed practical nurse is an interesting phase in nursing. There were strong feelings on the part of nurses who did not want licensed practical nurses and of practical nurses who fought bitterly about any law that would compel them to register. Katharine Shepard, for many years the director of the Household Nursing Association which was one of the early agencies to develop a good course for attendant nurses, has written an interesting account of the attendant movement.[3]

When a law was passed in Missouri in the early 'twenties which provided for the licensing of practical nurses, there was a battle royal between professional nurses and practical nurses who objected to being included in the law. Helen Wood, then director of the Washington University Training School for Nurses, prepared an article defending the law for *Caveat*, a small paper which it said "presents impartially both sides of proposed measures and public questions." Her opponent was Ann G. Maguire of the Under Graduate and Practical Nurses Association, who called the law "a menace to the public, because it gives a monopoly on nursing to the Graduate Nurses . . . The new law does away with the learned Practical Nurse; no longer may she hold herself out as a Nurse, she now becomes an Attendant who cares for the sick."[4]

In June, 1933, the League formally accepted as one of its functions a study of subsidiary workers, in cooperation with the ANA and NOPHN. Much interest was aroused in 1934 when Dr. Harlan H. Horner, Assistant Commissioner, proposed a plan for nursing education in New York state.[5] His report was based in large measure on a study by Leonore Bradley. Dr. Horner had sent a copy of the report to the League and indicated he would welcome an opinion on it. The report pointed out that it was estimated that there were more than 35,000 persons in New York State who were offering themselves to care for the sick but who were not licensed or recognized in any way by the state.

These persons varied from those who were without any experience and who had just decided to go into nursing, to trained nurses from other states who had dropped their title and practiced as free-lancers because they did not wish to take the licensing examination. Also, the education law in New York provided for the licensing of trained attendants, but this "had led nowhere." Among the remedial measures which Dr. Horner suggested was a law that no person might offer herself to care for the sick for hire without a license from the state. In amending the education law, provision would be made for the practical nurses who were presently practicing and who could present reasonable evidence of successful experience. He also suggested that in the future there be a new classification of Practical Nurse, and that a candidate for a license as a practical nurse be required to be a graduate of an approved high school, to pass a fitness and personality test prescribed by the Department of Education, and to pursue an approved course of study, largely practical, of one year in a registered school for practical nurses.

At a meeting of the Board of Directors of the NLNE held in January, 1935, correspondence was read from Dr. Horner of the New York State Department of Education which indicated that he would welcome an opinion from the NLNE of proposed plans for nursing education in New York. A motion was passed that a small committee be appointed by the chairman to consider Dr. Horner's report and to report later in the session. There was a good deal of discussion as to the wisdom of compulsory legislation which would include the subsidiary group.

One of the strong opponents to the licensing of subsidiary groups was Annie W. Goodrich. Miss Goodrich was invited to meet with the League Board. She stated that it was her belief that licensing of nursing care of the sick for hire should be held to the professionally qualified nurse. To include in the licensing provision the less qualified groups, she felt, would be to endorse rather than to prevent care of the sick by unqualified persons. The fundamental factor in the provision of adequate and qualified nursing for the sick, she said, is some form of social insurance through which such service would be available for all members of the community.[6] As secretary of the Board, I recorded the discussion, but there was one statement she made which I thought it wiser not to include in the official minutes. That statement was that to license this group was to "prostitute nursing." Her vivid language more or less shook me. After expressing her views, Miss Goodrich left the meeting. Later in that meeting, the board voted on my motion that we approve the principle that all persons who gave nursing service for hire should be licensed. One member of the Board voted "No." The Board disapproved, however, of the setting up of schools for the training of subsidiary workers unless there was control of the practice by the state.[7] It will be remembered that at that time there were a number of schools for the training of subsidiary workers throughout the country, and many of them were well-known.

Dr. Horner had asked the Board to comment on his recommendations and after the special committee reported, the board instructed me as secretary to write Dr. Horner. I believe my letter gives the gist of the committee's opinion. In this letter, dated January 28, 1935, I said, "As you know we stand for the highest type of nursing service to the community and believe unreservedly the public should be protected from the services of incompetent persons. At the present time the nursing profession is divided in its opinion on the desirability of licensing as nurses all those who give care to the sick for hire. We are, however, much concerned that all persons who are ill receive proper nursing care." The remainder of the letter was devoted to some statements about basic nursing education for professional nurses.[8]

In January, 1938, a motion of the Board of Directors was passed that we inform our state leagues "that in line with our certificate of incorporation which states that the object of this association shall be to consider all questions relating to nursing education . . . assist in furthering all matters pertaining to public health . . . aid in all measures for public good by cooperating with other bodies, educational, philanthropic and social, that we consider it important that our national and state leagues keep informed of those activities related to nursing which are being carried on by various organizations, such as state departments of education, and that they stand ready to advise on such activities as the occasion arises."[9] This action seemed at variance with the action taken by the Board of Directors of the ANA at its meeting on January 29, 1937, and sent to state presidents on February 19, 1937, that the Board wanted to go on record as having the following opinion "that when it seems expedient for nurses to serve on committees which have to do with the preparation of subsidiary workers, they should serve as individuals and not as representatives of organized nursing. Instances in which they would so serve should be governed by the local situation and by the practice which has heretofore existed in the community with regard to the question of nurses serving on committees for the discussion of problems which have community implications." The Board of the NLNE voted that the resolution we had previously passed be sent to the ANA either by letter or by having the president present it in person.[10] It will be seen therefore, that when the League committed itself to the principle of the preparation of subsidiary workers and their licensing, the ANA was on the opposite side of the fence.

An interesting development came in 1938 when private duty nurses called to the attention of the Boards of the ANA and the NLNE the fact that an eighteen-month course was being offered by the "————— Hospital School of Private Duty Nursing." The administrator of this hospital was a member of the Massachusetts Board of Registration in Nursing. A letter was sent by the presidents of the ANA and the NLNE to the ————— Hospital in which they expressed their opinion that no formal courses for the preparation of subsidiary workers should be approved until such time as a method for the control of the practice of subsidiary workers was devised. It also pointed out that the Boards deplored the use of the term "private duty nursing" in relation to graduates of an eighteen-month hospital course, because it was misleading to the public, and that "private duty nursing as a service rendered by a fully prepared nurse who is a graduate of a school of nursing which meets the minimum requirements set by law in the state, is registered in the state, and has, in addition, through experience developed special skill in the care of patients."[11] That school was shortly discontinued.

On the other side of the Atlantic, there was also lively discussion of the subsidiary worker. At the International Council of Nurses in London, in 1937, I presided at a meeting on this subject. In the heat of the discussion, when those in favor seemed to be getting the upper hand, I saw the person charged with admitting people to the hall suddenly go out. Back she came with Mrs. Bedford Fenwick, one of the founders of the ICN and the leader of the battle for state registration for nurses in England in the early part of the century. She came up on the platform. I greeted her courteously, but she immediately began a tirade against the registration of subsidiary workers. She was attempting to take the meeting out of my hands. But I held my ground and exercised my prerogative as the appointed chairman. Mrs. Fenwick was still vigorous in those days and as formidable an opponent as was Miss Goodrich. Her penchant for feather boas fascinated some of us. She always wore one, and seemed to have them in all hues, suitable for morning, afternoon or evening events.

I was highly amused recently to read a memorandum dated December, 1950, in which an administrator of a Boston hospital was trying to distinguish between nursing care and nursing service. He had this to say: "Licensed attendants is the answer. Five years ago, people concerned with this problem, recognizing the trend, pointed out that nursing is divided into two categories — nursing care and nursing service. By nursing care is meant the real scientific and professional duties that only a qualified nurse can perform. By nursing service is meant the myriad of duties that any reasonably intelligent girl can carry out, and this with a minimum of training. Unfortunately, it is this latter function by which the average patient, trustee, lay person judges nursing, and it consists of bedpan carrying, bed making, servicing trays, fixing flowers, greeting visitors, listing patients' clothing and valuables, and if in the home, preparing meals as well as tidying up the room and making the patient comfortable. All these duties can and must be done in the future by licensed attendants, and graduate nurses must have their work limited to nursing care which, as stated, is a scientific and professional work that only they can do."[12]

I wondered where he had been during the War, when nursing care was being given in institutions by trained practical nurses. The Commonwealth of Massachusetts, through its Approving Authority for Schools of Nursing, began to approve schools of practical nursing and to license practical nurses in 1944.

The effective contribution which had been made by practical nurses during the war years was recognized in *A Comprehensive Program for Nation-wide Action in the Field of Nursing,* issued by the National Planning Committee of the National Nursing Council for War Service.[13] It pointed out the need to study and define the functions and relationships of professional and practical nurses, to evaluate them in relation to the entire community nursing program, and to develop an understanding of the public's need for both types of nurses. It included schools of practical nursing in its program of nursing education, and stressed interpretation to the profession and public of the value of licensure for all who nurse for hire.

References

1. Newcomber, Mabel. *A Century of Higher Education.* Harper and Brothers, New York. 1959, p. 17.
2. Roberts, Mary M. *American Nursing.* The Macmillan Company, New York. 1954, p. 54.
3. Shepard, Katharine. "The First Thirty Years." Reprinted in *Annual Report, Household Nursing Association,* Boston. 1968.
4. Wood, Helen, and Maguire, Ann C. "Discussion. Nurse Practice Act in Missouri." *Caveat,* Vol. I. No. 5. St. Louis, Mo. October, 1922, p. 1.
5. Horner, Harlan H. *Nursing Education and Practice with Suggested Remedial Measures.* The University of the State of New York Press. 1934.
6. Minutes, NLNE Board of Directors. January, 1935, p. 8.
7. *Ibid.*
8. Goostray, Stella. Letter to Dr. Harland H. Horner. January 28, 1935.
9. Minutes, NLNE Board of Directors, January, 1938, p. 15.
10. *Ibid.*
11. Presidents, ANA and NLNE. Letter to a hospital disapproving of a School of Private Duty Nursing.
12. Memorandum. Hospital administrator discusses *Nursing and Nursing Service.*
13. National Planning Committee, National Nursing Council for War Service. *A Comprehensive Program for Nation-wide Action in the Field of Nursing.* July, 1943, pp. 5, 6.

Chapter Twelve

A WALL BEGINS TO TUMBLE

MORE professional solidarity which would manifest itself in a common endeavor to understand the problems of the whole profession and to participate actively in their solution was one of the basic needs to be met if nursing were to advance to new levels of effectiveness in the new social order which began in the middle of the 'thirties. There was one wall of separation within the profession in which we had hardly made a dent. I refer to the problems of the Negro nurse. For many years, membership in the ANA and the NLNE was not opened to all Negro nurses because of state organization limitations.

The ANA by-laws did not exclude Negro nurses from membership, but restriction came in 1916 when membership in the state association became the requirement for national membership. In 1940, the NLNE voted to grant individual membership to any qualified nurse who because of race was excluded from a state league. The ANA convention in the same year also discussed the question of individual membership, but it took eight years for favorable action. In 1948, there were eleven state associations that excluded Negro nurses. By 1952, seven associations of the eleven had responded affirmatively to ANA pressures. Whenever the subject was proposed, deep emotional reactions were aroused in the remaining four, especially among some of the delegates from Georgia. I wish I could think the four that eventually gave in did so because of the moral issues involved, but in my opinion, only the threat of separation from the ANA motivated these members.

There was little interaction between NACGN and the three so-called national nursing organizations. Even in the states which would admit Negro nurses to membership in the ANA and the NLNE, there were not many NACGN members. Back in the early 'twenties when I was working in Philadelphia, we had a local League of Nursing Education, as well as the state league. If I recall rightly, the first two Negro nurses who attended meetings of the local league asked me rather timidly if I would be willing to sign their application papers for membership in NLNE. This was something that I was exceedingly glad to do. Mabel Keaton Staupers in her book *No Time for Prejudice* refers to 1934 as the year when the pattern began to change through the broadening understanding of the problems facing Negro nurses that was developing among leaders responsible for suggesting policy and within the memberships of the three major nursing organizations themselves.

The League Board, at its meeting in April, 1934, recognized that there was little up-to-date information known to them on the opportunities open to Negro nurses in the different forms of community service such as public health nursing, private duty, and hospital work, as well as the present status of Negro schools of nursing and the number of students enrolled in these schools. We sent a communication to the Conference on Fundamental Problems of Negro Education, called by Dr. Zook, U. S. Commissioner of Education, urging that it use its influence in securing funds to make a survey of the status of Negro nursing service and nursing education, and stating that the League would cooperate in such a project.[1]

In 1939, the National League of Nursing Education had its convention in New Orleans. A communication was received by the Board from Estelle Massey Riddle of the National Association of Colored Graduate Nurses protesting the fact that Negro nurses attending the League sessions had to make use of the hotel service entrance.[2] The League president, who was then Nellie Hawkinson, and I as secretary were instructed by the Board to confer with the manager of the hotel in relation to this matter. We saw the assistant manager, and made, of course, no impression on him with our request that all members and guests use the same entrance. He told us that the procedure they followed was standard rule of hotels in the South. The president replied to him that we wished to register a protest and that such requirements would be a factor in considering future invitations to the League to meet in hotels below the Mason-Dixon line. Some of us also met with the Negro nurses and explained how sorry we were that this kind of treatment was accorded to them.[3] So far as I know, the NLNE never held another convention in the South.

One of the vivid images I retain of the separation was that of a meeting in Hollywood, Florida, when I spoke to the State Association on National Defense. Seated before me on one side of the room were the members of the National Association of Colored Graduate Nurses, and on the other side the white nurses. I assured the members of the NACGN that their association was a participating organization in the National Nursing Council for Defense on exactly the same terms as any other participating group. The situation made me physically upset, as I had evidence when I rushed to my hotel room after the meeting. And I never shall forget the cool drink that Lucy Germain, who was at the convention representing the *American Journal of Nursing*, brought to my room.

It is a matter of history that the National Asociation of Colored Graduate Nurses was dissolved in 1951 after forty years of patient, valiant and courageous struggle for full and equal status for the Negro nurse in the professional organization. Not all of the problems were solved and I doubt if they are yet solved, but I think it should be recorded that the National Nursing Council for War Service was a very important factor in helping to solve the problems of the Negro nurse, both graduate and student, in civilian and military life during World War II and for future years. But more of this later.

References

1. Minutes, NLNE Board of Directors. April, 1934, pp. 2, 3.
2. Minutes, NLNE Board of Directors. April, 1939, p. 12.
3. *Ibid.*

[113]

Chapter Thirteen

GIRDING THE PROFESSION FOR WAR SERVICE

O N Monday, September 4, 1939, the front page headlines in the *New York Times* were: "British Blockade Germany, French Speed War Plans; Berlin Reports Swift Advances on All Polish Fronts." "Roosevelt Asks Nation to Observe True Neutrality." Roosevelt: "There will be no blackout of peace in the United States."

Before the month of September was over, Miss Beard, in behalf of the Advisory Committee of the American Red Cross Nursing Service, asked the NLNE to appoint a committee first to help increase enrollment in the First Reserve, and second, to set up a plan to be used to assist in expanding the number of desirable students admitted to schools of nursing to ensure that a larger number would be graduated.[1] The urgency of Miss Beard's request prompted the Headquarters Committee of NLNE to appoint a temporary committee to act until the Board meeting in January. A letter went to the director of every school from the president of NLNE asking them to stimulate enrollment of students in the American Red Cross Nursing Service. The committee appointed at the January Board meeting prepared a plan to be presented at the convention in May, and arranged that at the Advisory Council meeting there be reports from directors of schools on ways to encourage senior students to join the Red Cross Nursing Service after graduation. Interestingly, one of the suggestions in the plan for increasing the number of students was "to consider the advisability of reopening the Army School of Nursing, if the need for qualified nurses could not be met in other ways."[2]

By May, the war news from Europe had the people of the United States on edge. A telegram signed by the presidents of ANA (Stimson), NOPHN (Ross), and NLNE (Goostray) was sent to President Roosevelt, assuring him that the nursing profession wanted to "offer their strength and support in any nursing activity in which they could be of service" in the crisis.

That summer, the Department of Studies of NLNE worked on a study for the Red Cross on the estimated number of students who would graduate between 1940 and 1945 from all state-accredited schools of nursing, the number of schools meeting Red Cross Nursing Service requirements, the number meeting NOPHN requirements, the number of schools, as of June, 1940, complying with the provisions of the NOPHN, and the number of schools complying with the provisions of the Red Cross Nursing Service.[3] There was a response from ninety-three percent of the schools.

The Nursing Council on National Defense Is Launched

On July 10, 1940, Isabel Stewart, as the newly-elected president of the NLNE, wrote me regarding "the need of some official nursing committtee or commission to think through the position that nurses should take with respect to national defense and the many adjustments that may be called for within the next few months. The committee appointed by the NLNE to work with the American Red Cross is not representative enough for the thing I have in mind . . . I believe we should have such a commission or board that is representative of the nursing profession *as a whole* and that it should be at work now, and not wait until Miss Beard calls on us to do something in connection with the American Red Cross." Realizing the urgency of Miss Stewart's request and suggestion, at supper on the day I received the letter I talked it over with Sophie Nelson. Miss Stewart said Sophie Nelson was "one of the best thinkers of our group." I also wrote Nellie Hawkinson, since she was the chairman of the NLNE's committee to work with the Red Cross. I suggested to Sophie Nelson and Nellie Hawkinson that Julia Stimson, as the president of the American Nurses' Association, should be asked to take the initial step in calling a conference. They agreed. I wrote her on July 19, 1940, that we agreed with Isabel Stewart that there should be a committee "which would represent our three national nursing organizations . . . and also represent the whole profession in working with all federal government groups, the American Red Cross, and any national committee representing other professional groups." A copy of my letter went to Miss Ross, who was president of the NOPHN.[4] Julia Stimson lost no time, and on July 29, just short of three weeks from the date of Miss Stewart's first letter to me, representatives of five national nursing organizations — ANA, NOPHN, NLNE, NACGN, ACSN, and representatives of several Federal agencies — Army Nurse Corps, Navy Nurse Corps, Children's Bureau, USPHS, Divisions of State Relations and of Hospitals, Nursing Service, Veterans Administration Nursing Service, Department of Indian Affairs and the ARCNS met in New York. By the end of that day, the Nursing Council on National Defense was on its way.

It had defined its functions as a planning body to determine the role of nurses in national defense and their most effective use, to unify all nursing activities directly or indirectly related to national defense, to ensure the maintenance of a high quality of nursing education and nursing service, and to act as a clearinghouse for all agencies concerned with nursing activities in national defense.

The Council had no money except what the national organizations and their state units could give from their budgets. Julia Stimson agreed to act as chairman and Mrs. Alma Scott as secretary (there was no election), and although it was not an ANA project per se, but a Council whose responsibilities were to be shared by all the agencies involved, the ANA generously shared its offices with the Council for over a year. It was agreed that in working out projects we would as far as possible use the usual channels of the organizations involved.

The first project of the new Council was to ask the USPHS and the WPA to sponsor a census of graduate registered nurses. They agreed, and the three national nursing organizations acted as co-sponsors. We had to know how many graduate nurses there would be available for military and civilian needs. We could not use the figures from the 1940 census, since the tabulations made no distinction between graduate and student nurses. And using a familiar channel to reach the registered nurses all over the country, the state associations of the ANA became the working units in getting the needed information.

The second project was a plan proposed by a Committee for Educational Policies, with Isabel Stewart as chairman, to expand the present nursing education program to provide for national defense needs. This involved a Federal appropriation for nursing education. We wanted the Office of Education to try to secure this appropriation. Isabel Stewart talked the matter over with the Commissioner of Education. He was interested but wanted the proposal to come through his office rather than through the Committee. He invited Isabel Stewart to go to Washington, but not as chairman of the Committee, to prepare a proposal for the Office of Education.

It was typical of Isabel Stewart that she would not accede to the Commissioner of Education's request to go to Washington to prepare a proposal unless she were free to consult with the members of the Committee who had worked with her. The guiding genius of the Committee, of course, was Isabel Stewart, and she spent two to three weeks in Washington working on the proposal, using as a basis the points the Committee had agreed on.[5]

The proposal as prepared for the Office of Education was rejected, much to the disappointment of the Committee. As a member of the Committee, I had a copy of the proposal. It was marked "Tentative and Confidential." I gave my copy to the Schlesinger Library (formerly the Women's Archives) of Radcliffe College, and through their courtesy a copy is available in the Nursing Archive, Mugar Library, Boston University.[6] The Committee did not give up. The plan was revamped somewhat and was then channeled through the USPHS with the blessing of the Health and Medical Committee of the Council of National Defense, one of whose subcommittees was on nursing. (Mary Beard was chairman). And nursing's good friend Congresswoman Frances Payne Bolton vigorously supported an appropriation act which provided for nursing education.

I had my first introduction to legislative procedure on a federal level at a hearing on the bill as president of the NLNE. The relaxed mood of members of the committee responsible for the hearing when I appeared astonished me. They wandered in and out at will. The act, passed by the 77th Congress, became effective July 1, 1941, and covered a two-year period. It provided funds to increase the enrollment in schools of nursing and to prepare teachers and establish refresher courses for inactive nurses to enable them to return to active practice. For the first time in the history of the United States Federal funds were specifically appropriated for nursing education. During World War I Federal funds were used for the Army School of Nursing, but these came from appropriations allotted to the Army. The wise administration and counseling of this first program for nursing education under Pearl McIver and her associates, is sometimes lost sight of in the more glamorous program of the Cadet Nurse Corps.

After the act was passed, the Committee on Educational Policies asked to be dissolved. It was later re-called temporarily to make recommendations concerning the modification of its original proposal to meet new needs. Thereafter, the NLNE appointed a Committee on Educational Problems in War Times which assumed responsibility for assisting schools. This action was in accord with the Nursing Council's policy to use the channel of the professional organization involved in a specific activity.

War Calls for Reorganization of the Council

Fortunately for the National Nursing Council and all who were associated with it during the active years of the war, Mrs. Elmira

Bears Wickenden became the executive secretary, and the Council moved into its own quarters before the bombing of Pearl Harbor. The war naturally brought many new problems and called for a reorganization of the Council. The Kellogg Foundation had generously agreed to be the major financial support of the Council, and this required the establishment of an incorporated body eligible to receive funds. Legal steps were taken to incorporate the Council in New York as the National Nursing Council for War Service. Heretofore, no election of officers had taken place, but now such an election was required by law. At the end of the July meeting in 1942, there was a reluctant new president, Stella Goostray. I had had no time to think about it, and despite my expressed reluctance to accept, Mary Beard who had nominated me told me in the meeting that I had no choice in the matter. "It is your wartime responsibility," said she. Believe me, I hated to return to Boston and tell my Children's Hospital family what had happened. I would be away even more often.

USPHS Division of Nursing Education, National Association for Practical Nurse Education, International Council of Nurses, American Association of Industrial Nurses, and sixteen members at large were added to the Council, and the Council and the AHA set up a cooperative relationship. Of course there were disagreements and misunderstandings, and sometimes strong emotion was generated. Means and ends were often confused. It was no wonder, since we had for years been concerned with our own little bailiwick of interest, and each organization jealously guarded what it thought was its preserves. It was my feeling that when we had agreed upon principles we should maintain a flexibility about the ways of making them effective, and as president I held to this tenet. Our responsibility was to strive for such unity in our profession as would make it possible to render the nursing service that the country needed. As I look back on those days, I am satisfied that we really did achieve a good measure of unity.

Recruitment for a "Proud Profession"

It was hoped by the Council that it might be possible to enroll

55,000 young women in 1942. But the hope was not realized. Dr. George Baehr, medical director of the Office of Civil Defense, and Surgeon General Parran of the USPHS called a conference to discuss steps to be taken to recruit more students, to accelerate nurse training programs and to train subsidiary workers. The NLNE had already recommended an accelerated program. Of course, there was talk of reviving the Army School of Nursing. Another suggestion was that there be an "umbrella school" under the sponsorship of all the Federal services. Naturally, one of the chief advocates for the Army School of Nursing was Annie Goodrich. The times called for a new approach. Finally, the creation of a Cadet Nurse Corps was suggested, and the combined effort of the Council and the government's subcommittee was the catalyst to start the action.

Of course we wanted to get Annie Goodrich on our side, too. Some of the statements she was quoted as having made indicated that she thought neither the consultants on nursing education in the USPHS nor those of us who were the officers of the organizations involved knew much about nursing education. She had forgotten that she had been a good teacher through both the spoken and written word, and that some of her philosophy had been absorbed by a younger generation. Not too long ago, Pearl McIver reminded me of the strategy used to swing Miss Goodrich over. The strategy was planned by a few leaders on the way home from a meeting in Chicago. We agreed to suggest to Surgeon General Parran that he invite Miss Goodrich to Washington for a short period to act as a consultant. The strategy worked. I remember returning from Washington when we sat together until she reached New Haven, and it was a very delightful time. On that occasion she told me that she did not believe nurses whose only experience was in public health nursing were competent to direct a university school.

Mrs. Bolton introduced a bill in the House of Representatives, and Senator Thomas introduced a similar bill in the Senate which created the U. S. Cadet Nurse Corps. There were open hearings on both bills, and my testimony was offered as president of NLNE. I do not know why I filed additional testimony after the hearing but

I did.[7] Much to my surprise, when I went to file the written material shortly after noon, there was a sign on the office door "Gone to lunch." So Washington copied the little country store. On the evening of the Senate hearing, Mrs. Bolton, Senator Thomas, James Hamilton, president of AHA, and I broadcast from Washington. (The following summer in Blue Hill, Maine, I met a lumberjack I knew who hailed me with "I heerd you on the radio about them nurses." He had received the broadcast in his little shack far in the back woods.) The bill was passed without a dissenting vote in the Congress.

Box 88, New York, was the address of the clearing bureau of the Council which handled requests for information from thousands of young women who wanted to know how to "join a proud profession." This program had a great appeal for young women. A snappy, gray-wool uniform, with touches of scarlet and silver buttons, was designed by Mollie Parnis, a well-known New York stylist. A jaunty beret, a raincoat, an overcoat, a shoulder bag, and a summer uniform completed the outfit. And when the War Advertising Council got into the action, all the stops of sales promotion were pulled. Besides the accoutrements and the stipend furnished by the Cadet Corps, gifts of all kinds, from lipstick to New Testaments went to each member of the Corps. As president of the Council, I was co-signer with Surgeon General Parran of all checks which paid for the uniforms in the period in which students were admitted to the Corps, the Council being designated as the purchasing agent for USPHS. For once in my life, I felt like a millionaire. No students were admitted after October, 1945. The official history of the U. S. Cadet Nurse Corps was published in 1950.[8]

Despite any lure from the great advantages offered, it is my belief that thousands of young women entered the Corps because they wanted to be part of the national war effort. And one thing is certain, the U. S. Cadet Nurse Corps gave a lift to nursing education. Of course, there were weaknesses in the program, but they were not unrecognized by those who planned and carried it out. We were at war, and compromises had to be made.

When James Hamilton, president of the AHA, reported to his

association about the U. S. Cadet Nurse Corps, he said, "United we stand." We had some pretty spirited discussions getting to that united stage. Many hospital administrators were averse to accelerating the program, which was obligatory in the Corps, because it meant the loss of senior students during the last six months of training, when they would be of most service to a hospital. Mr. Hamilton was well liked and respected by the nurses, and we were fortunate to have him on the executive committee, but we did not always agree with him or with the efforts of the AHA to direct our ways. At one of our conferences, he intimated that the nurses were presuming to dictate all of the adjustments. Something he said riled me, and my reply was that we had been in bondage long enough, and like the Children of Israel we were on the march into the Promised Land. Now, more than twenty-five years later, although we have not fully entered the promised land of a self-determining profession, we have at least reached the border.

A Wrong Finally Righted

In 1940, according to the United States census, there were approximately 7,000 Negro nurses in the United States. When World War II was declared, very few Negro nurses were accepted by the Army Nurse Corps. A quota was maintained, and there was segregation of these nurses. This was a matter which seriously disturbed the National Nursing Council for War Service. Letters were written to the Surgeons General of the Army and Navy Medical Corps asking why Negro nurses were not accepted on the same basis as any other American nurse who met the requirements. A reply came from the Surgeon General of the Army asking how general the practice was of using white and Negro nurses in the same situation. And a list was sent to him of the hospitals throughout the country in which Negro and white nurses worked amiably side by side caring for white and

Negro patients. No more was heard from General Kirk. The only response from the Surgeon General of the Navy was a formal acknowledgement without comment.[9] Having waited six months with no improvement in conditions, the Council then appointed a special committee, of which I was chairman, to seek personal interviews with both Surgeons General. As I recall, Elmira Wickenden and Anna D. Wolf went with me to Washington to make the calls. We saw only an Assistant Surgeon General of the Army, but did see the Surgeon General of the Navy. We asked our pertinent — one would think it was impertinent, from the response we got — question, "Why are Negro nurses not being appointed to the Nurse Corps of the Army and Navy on the same basis as other American nurses who meet the professional qualifications." We got no encouragement, and my impression of the Surgeon General of the Navy was that we might as well have been talking to a stuffed shirt.

Up to this time, no publicity had been given by the Council to this serious situation. But now we were out "to tell the world." We were determined to continue our efforts as long as necessary, to remedy the situation. We got support from the NACGN, who in turn interested other organizations of Negroes and other influential people to work towards the same end. Eventually we won out, and there were six hundred Negro nurses in the Army Nurse Corps at the height of the war. The Navy accepted its first Negro nurse in 1945, after about two years of continued hammering energized by the Council. I believe this first Navy nurse was a younger sister of Mrs. Staupers.

The Council's Negro Unit

The problems of the Negro graduate nurse and of young Negro girls who wanted to obtain a good education in nursing had become so pressing that in 1943, as an experiment for a year, the General Education Board of the Rockefeller Foundation financed a unit in the Council to be devoted to these problems. It was directed by Mrs. Estelle Massey Riddle (later Mrs. Osborn), a highly qualified and knowledgeable consultant. In the words of Mrs. Riddle, "The establishment of the Negro unit in the Council provided the first opportunity for Negro nurses' participation on an administrative level within a professional nursing organization working for all nurses, and probably the first opportunity to broaden the functioning of general administrative units to consider the needs of the Negro people."[10]

The experimental period brought such telling results, not only in the specific area for which it was organized, but also in its contribution to the general activities of the Council, that a larger grant was given by the General Board, and the Kellogg Foundation, which so generously supported the general work of the Council, made a grant to cover the salary of an assistant consultant, Miss Alma Vessells. Not the least of its many accomplishments was the unit's success in helping Hampton Institute establish a collegiate program in nursing. With the help of these consultants, twenty-one of the twenty-eight schools for Negro students had improved their standards sufficiently to be eligible for the U. S. Cadet Nurse Corps. At the beginning of the war, fourteen schools of nursing admitted both white and Negro students. Their number had almost tripled at its end.

By the introduction of two Negro nurses to the NNCWS's staff, a new precedent was established, and Negro nurses were appointed to the staffs of the national nursing organizations.

The plan for action by the profession following the war, as outlined by its post-war planning committee, pointed out that the program related to all nurses, professional and practical, Negro and white, men and women. The president of the NACGN at that time, Frances F. Gaines, noted that their organization was deeply conscious that for the first time the nursing profession included all nurses in the development of a plan for its future.[11]

Post-war Planning

The profession may have been slow in getting plans formulated in relation to national defense, but this was not the case with post-war planning for nurses who would return from overseas service and with comprehensive guidance for the profession. Each of the nursing organizations established a post-war planning committee, and their suggestions were pooled and incorporated in the Council's plan. The result was the publication of the pamphlet, *A Comprehensive Program for Nation-wide Action in the Field of Nursing*.[12] Many of these plans were put into action and resulted in the advancement of nursing service to the community, improved education of nurses, and the promotion of schools for practical nurses and licensure of their graduates.

One of the studies which I particularly hoped would follow the war was a study of nursing education. So much had happened to start a change in the traditional pattern and so much more was needed to be done, that I had talked with Mrs. Wickenden about it on one of our trips to Washington together. I became so engrossed in the idea that I could not find my ticket when the conductor came to collect it, and I had to pay another fare.[13] It was a hope realized when the Post-war Planning Committee of NLNE, chaired by Anna Wolf, with the approval of the Board of Directors of the League, included the study in the plans they submitted to the Council's Post-war Planning Committee. Another recommendation was the coordination of all the accreditation activities of the professional organizations.[14]

Facing a Draft

During the latter part of 1944, the Surgeon General of the Army kept pressing for more nurses but gave no reason why. And then came a startling announcement from the President of the United States. "I urge," said Mr. Roosevelt in his annual message to Congress, early in January, 1945, "that the Selective Service Act be amended to provide for the induction of nurses into the armed forces." That was a startling announcement, to say the least. The three national nursing organizations, as well as the NNCWS were ready to support a national service act which would include all women as well as men, but, as NNCWS telegraphed the President, we believed drafting only registered nurses would tend to discourage the volunteer recruitment for the Army and Navy. However, we seconded his appeal to nurses to enlist "at once" pending legislation. We also asked him to appeal at his next press conference to physicians, industries, hospitals, all agencies, patients, and the public to give up all but most essential nursing service in view of the immediate military needs.

The five months from January 1 to May 30, 1945, were nerve-wracking months for the NNCWS and the agencies it involved. The President had declared himself in favor of a draft for nurses, and new Army orders called for complete reclassification of nurses in civil positions. This announcement came without warning to us and without the acquiesence of the War Manpower Commission under whose aegis the Procurement and Assignment Service operated. A news-paper report called attention to the protest made by the NNCWS at its meeting in January, and the letter sent over my signature to Paul McNutt, chairman of the War Manpower Commission, pointed out that minimum staffs must be maintained in schools of nursing, and that in 1944 the schools of nursing had admitted seventy-eight percent more students than in 1940. "These students not only offer the only assurance the armed forces have of an adequate pool from which to draw nurses in the years ahead, but are actually doing a large share of civilian nursing today."[15] Our anxiety was relieved on May 30 when the threat of the draft was withdrawn.

War-time Travel

A cartoon in one of the Boston papers during the present Viet Nam war days showed two matronly ladies standing at the open door of a car filled with GI's. The legend was "Oh, come on Harriet

. . . If they whistle at us, they whistle at us." It reminded me very vividly of the night Ruth Sleeper and I were sitting in a railroad day coach on our way to a hearing in Washington. Two GI's turned their seat over to face us, and most of the night their feet were on either side of us. I suppose they thought they could stretch out better and probably thought two ladies could do that much for their country. When the hawker came around with ice cream, they wanted to treat us. It was the first time I had ever known Ruth Sleeper to refuse ice cream. But she was very grateful in the morning when I brought out a thermos of coffee and a couple of oranges. I had traveled on night trains so many times and had had difficulty getting breakfast in the stations, that I had learned to be forearmed with food, and also with a small, pencil-sized flashlight, for the times in the evening when we reached our destination in a blackout. That flashlight gave enough light to show the way out of the darkened coach. And more than one fellow traveler thanked me for the light.

Often I was the only woman or civilian in a car of GI's. On one occasion, a GI fell asleep and dropped his head on my shoulder, and there he slept peacefully from just below Buffalo to Albany. I told that story at a Joint Board meeting, and my confreres thought I was spoofing, but I was not.

Sometimes one had very little notice about meetings. On the occasion referred to above the USPHS office telephoned at six p.m. asking me to come to Washington on the night train and to try to get Ruth Sleeper, the new president of the National League of Nursing Education, to come also to testify at a Senate hearing. Alma Scott was there for the ANA and I for the NNCWS. A bill had been introduced to create a division of nursing under the Public Health Service Act for July 1, 1944. The afternoon before the bill was to go to the House, Pearl McIver, I believe, discovered that some important provisions for equal rank for nurses in the USPHS had been omitted. A hearing on the bill was slated for the next morning under the chairmanship of Lister Hill. Well, we testified, and the omissions were restored.[16] Traveling in those days was a bit rugged. More often than not we had to travel at night, and there were no Pullmans or dining cars. If we were going for a day only, we could not get a hotel room, and we used the public washrooms in the station to freshen up.

A Battle Flag for the *USS Higbee*

It was my privilege to present to the *USS Higbee,* when it was commissioned on January 27, 1945, at the Charlestown Navy Yard, a battle flag on behalf of the National Nursing Council for War Service. For the first time in its history, the U. S. Navy put in commission a combat vessel named in honor of a Navy Nurse. It was a memorable day in the history of the nursing profession, for we considered that a great honor had been conferred on us by the action of the United States Navy in naming a ship in honor of one of our members, Lenah Sutcliffe Higbee, the second superintendent of the Navy Nurse Corps. The flag was presented in memory of Mrs. Higbee and in honor of the 9,000 nurses then serving in the Navy Nurse Corps. While I spoke the words of presentation to the Commanding Officer, two nurses stood at my right holding the folded flag. One was a Navy nurse and the other, a Cadet Corps nurse, was one of my own senior students who was spending her last six months at the naval hospital in Chelsea.

At the close of the war, Lindsey Williamson, Commander of the *USS Higbee,* returned the battle flag, and his accompanying letter, addressed to me, said: "The sight of that flag flying on August 15, 1945, was something no one on the *Higbee* will ever forget. Engineers and lower deck ratings got permission to come topside, and the spontaneous cheer each one of them gave upon seeing it waving in the stiff breeze made a chill run up and down my spine. I don't think the United States has anything to worry about as long as we have men like the *Higbee* crew sailing the seas for us."[17]

The letter and the battle flag were sent to the Navy Nurse Corps, and they are now in the Navy Museum, Annapolis, Maryland.

It had been planned to dissolve the Council within six months after the declaration of peace. Money was low, and the grant from the Kellogg Foundation expired at the end of the war. However, there was still unfinished business. The words "for War Service" were legally deleted in November, 1945, and the Council continued for three years as the National Nursing Council. I had served as president of the corporation during its life as the National Nursing Council for War Service (July, 1942–November, 1945). In January, 1946, Sophie Nelson succeeded me and remained president until the Council dissolved in November, 1948, following the publication of *Nursing for the Future,* Dr. Esther L. Brown's brilliant study of nursing education.[18]

Unfortunately, the records of the Nursing Council in its three stages were destroyed, but not before an official history could be written by Hope Newell, who had been on the staff of the Council. The National Nursing Council History Committee, under whose aegis the history was prepared, consisted of Marjorie B. Davis, Stella Goostray, Alma C. Haupt, Ruth Sleeper, and Sophie C. Nelson. Mrs. Almira B. Wickenden was chairman.[19] The history restricted its scope to those efforts instigated by the group planning made possible through the Council, and particularly to those projects for which the Council had the major responsibility or in which it cooperated with national nursing organizations or Federal agencies.[20]

The amount of volunteer service given to the Council was tremendous. During the period of its existence as a War Council, 1942-1945, nearly fifty active committees were at work on war problems and post-war planning; their members gave unstintedly of their time and talents. Susan C. Francis, a former president of the ANA, moved over from Philadelphia to New York and gave full-time volunteer service for the duration of the war. Mrs. Wickenden was awarded the Medal of Merit, an honor richly deserved for her outstanding services far beyond the duties required of an executive secretary.

My honest opinion, as I stated at the final meeting at which I presided, was that "During the period of the war, the nursing profession with the allied professional groups and lay public have worked together as never before with unity of purpose to accomplish that which was in the interest of the common good. Now is the appointed time to make our choice as to whether we shall go on working together for what is best for nursing, both in its relation to the nursing profession and those whom it serves, or whether we shall be concerned mainly with our boundary lines of organization. Some way surely can be found, if we approach the problem open-mindedly and objectively, to pool our thinking, work out our plans, and put them into operation as a united group."[21]

The NLNE Meets Present Needs But Looks to the Future

This chapter began with the League's response to the urgent request of the ARCNS for help. Now we return to the League's program during the war. When the rumbles of war began to echo, there was an immediate cry from hospital administrators to cut down on the curriculum. That, in their opinion, was the only solution to the problem of servicing the nursing needs of the hospitals. We had other ideas. When we were working on ways to preserve good service in the hospitals and at the same time preserve good nursing education for the students, I was asked to speak at the dinner meeting of the Massachusetts Hospital Association. The president was an aggressive and outspoken individual who used the occasion to express his views in no uncertain terms about nursing education and what it should be in wartime. He did not hesitate to use "cuss words." Then he introduced me, and I turned to him and said in what I hoped was a dulcet tone, "Dr. ————, I know all those words and can use them as well as you can, but I don't think I need to. My arguments need no reinforcement." And the crowd roared. Father McGowan, an administrator in one of the Catholic hospitals who later held a national office in one of the Catholic organizations in Washington, reminded me whenever I saw him in after-years of "the night you bested Dr. _____." Later on, at a convention of the American Hospital Association, when I spoke on educational problems in war-times and on behalf of the U. S. Cadet Nurse Corps, I saw my friend of the "cuss words" come into the meeting. After the meeting was over, he made a point to speak to me, and said, "That was a good address." So perhaps I helped to convert him.

Anecdotes are permissible in personal memoirs to break the monotony of serious matters, but it is important to point out how the League helped to meet the nursing problems of the war. The League urged the schools to accelerate their programs, to prune the curriculum wherever it was possible, to hold out for essentials, making sure they were essentials, to state our principles with forthright simplicity, and having stated them to hold fast to them. We also encouraged state and local leagues, in states where practical nurses or nursing attendants were licensed, to lend their support in recruiting candidates for the approved schools and in fostering the employment of the graduates under the conditions which would safeguard the care of the patients.

In the acceleration of the program and adjustment of the curriculum, schools were given detailed help, especially in a series of bulletins under the general title *Nursing Education in War Time.* They were issued under the aegis of the League's Committee on Educational Problems in War Time whose chairman was Nellie Hawkinson Each bulletin was written by a different member of the Committee. Ruth Harrington, a member of the faculty of the University of Minnesota School of Nursing, spent two-and-a-half months at Headquarters, involved in the arduous details of planning for and publishing the first bulletin. After Miss Harrington's return to Minnesota, Blanche Pfefferkorn served as editor of the bulletins.

We had geared our schools to the service demands of the war. We had made compromises with our eyes open to all the dangers which the pressure of war forced on us. But we were not content to have the conditions remain in which students carried the bulk of the nursing service and the clinical experience was based on hospital needs.

As the president's report pointed out in 1944, neither the pressure of the war nor the results of compromises were responsible for all our educational difficulties or for the economic problems which followed in their wake. There had always been the tendency in nursing education to emphasize training and technical skills. The question was asked, "Is not the time near at hand when we can provide a broad professional program which will advance nursing to new levels of effectiveness?"

No adequate program could be set up for the practice of good nursing in any of its major fields unless we provided a basic preparation, founded on sound educational principles, which included all types of clinical services and at the same time broadened nurses' appreciation of the pressing social and economic factors which are part of individual and community living.[22] If nursing was to attract the kind of young women that were needed, changes had also to be made in the personnel policies of agencies which employed graduate nurses. Such changes had to give increased recognition to them as professional persons with all the demands and desires of human beings to lead as normal a life as possible, and had to enable them to choose the conditions under which they lived and what they ate.[23] Some of these things have come to pass, but not all.

In 1943, the League celebrated its fiftieth anniversary as an organization. Two noteworthy events marked the anniversary: the admission of non-nurse members to the League, and the establishment of the Mary Adelaide Nutting Award for Leadership in Nursing. The award was designed by the famous woman sculptor, Melvina Hoffman. The Award is now given by the National League for Nursing.

The League did not hold a convention in 1944 but did have its annual meeting in Buffalo. The closing meeting of that session was a moving one for me, for the audience by a rising vote endorsed a resolution on behalf of the Board of Directors, presented by Isabel Stewart, expressing its appreciation of my services as president.[24] Never could I have gone through those years without the strength which had come from the whole-hearted commitment of the League staff, its Board, and its committees in our endeavors to preserve the integrity of nursing education, and at the same time meet the nursing needs in a time of war. It was a privilege to have served the League as its president, but gladly did I hand the gavel to Ruth Sleeper. That meeting ended on a very solemn note. It was a time of extreme anxiety and tension, for the invasion of Normandy was at hand, and we stood for one minute in silence to remember the men and women in the armed forces who were in the shadow of great danger.

References

1. *46th Annual Report*, NLNE. 1940, p. 100.
2. *47th Annual Report*, NLNE. 1941, pp. 11, 118.
3. *Ibid*, p. 37.
4. Personal correspondence, Isabel M. Stewart, Julia Stimson, Stella Goostray.
5. *47th Annual Report*, NLNE. 1941, p. 63.
6. Committee on Educational Policies, National Nursing Council. Copy of proposal submitted for Federal funds. 1941.
7. Goostray, Stella. Additional testimony filed following hearing on proposed U. S. Student Nurse Cadet Corps.
8. *Federal Security Agency. The United States Student Cadet Corps and the Nursing Training Program, 1943-1948.* USPHS Publication, No. 38. U. S. Government Printing Office, Washington, D. C. 1950.
9. Newell, Hope. *History of the National Nursing Council.* Distributed by NOPHN. 1951, p. 46.
10. National Planning Committee. *A Comprehensive Program for Nation-wide Action in the Field of Nursing.* NNCWS. 1945, p. 5.
11. Newell, Hope. *History of the National Nursing Council.* Distributed by NOPHN. 1951, pp. 49, 50.
12. National Planning Committee. *A Comprehensive Program for Nation-wide Action in the Field of Nursing,* NNCWS. 1945, p. 10.
13. Letter, Mrs. Homer Wickenden to Stella Goostray, November 20, 1968.
14. *51st Annual Report.* NLNE. 1945, pp. 91, 92.
15. *The New York Times,* January 30, 1945, p. 10.

16. Memorandum, Pearl McIver to Stella Goostray, March, 1967.

17. Letter, Commanding Officer *USS Higbee,* to Stella Goostray, October 15, 1945. See also Goostray Collection, National Nursing Council for War Service. Folder 27, Box 4.

18. Brown, Esther Lucille *Nursing for the Future.* Russell Sage Foundation, New York. 1948.

19. Newell, Hope. *History of the National Nursing Council.* Distributed by NOPHN. 1951, p. 114.

20. *Ibid.* p. ii

21. *Ibid.* p. 90.

22. *50th Annual Report.* NLNE. 1944, p. 52.

23. *Ibid.* p. 53.

24. *Ibid.* p. 172.

Chapter Fourteen

CHANGES TO MEET NEW CHALLENGES

THE Associated Alumnae had not long been organized, giving us two professional organizations, the American Society of Superintendents of Training Schools for Nurses and the Associated Alumnae, when there was discussion as to amalgamation of the two organizations. But the Society of Superintendents did not want to give up their organization of nursing educators with its rather restricted membership. From time to time, the question would crop up, especially after the two organizations were joined by a third, the National Organization for Public Health Nursing. In 1939, a state association petitioned the American Nurses Association to consider the matter of amalgamation, and forthwith a committee was appointed with Mary Beard as chairman.

Because of the war, the matter was deferred somewhat, but the Joint Boards voted in January, 1944, that the national professional organizations should undertake a joint survey of their organizations regarding structure, administration, functions and facilities, to determine whether a more effective means could be found to promote and carry forward the strongest possible program for nursing and nurses.[1] That program, in my opinion, involved achieving greater professional unity, meeting the constantly growing demand for nursing services, and enlisting the active interest of the community in understanding nursing needs and in helping to meet them.

A firm of sociological experts was engaged, and this firm made its report at the 1946 convention of the three sponsoring organizations. An extremely complicated structure was proposed, for which the profession was not ready. That was the end of the structure as proposed by the Raymond Rich Associates. But the organizations continued the study through a joint Structure Committee. The Committee was enlarged by including representatives from the NACGN, the ACSN, and the American Association of Industrial Nurses, who were now members of the National Nursing Council. The Council was already planning post-war developments, and naturally there was a close relation between this program and the structure of the organizations that would function in carrying it out.

There were two points of view, one favoring a single organization and the other pleading for two. A job assigned to me one summer by the committee was to work out some by-laws through which we could have one organization yet provide some way for having non-nurse participation. The NOPHN representatives argued for an organization that would give full privileges of membership to non-nurse members. The NOPHN had been organized on that premise, and it was so successful in establishing community relationships and active participation in the organization's work that it was quite understandable that it should demand that this should continue. The League also had non-nurse members. But the difficulty was that we were members of the ICN. It was Pearl McIver, then president of the ANA, who turned the tide to two organizations.

Miss McIver reported that she had just come from Europe, and she felt very doubtful that there would be any change in thinking on the part of the ICN as to non-nurse membership. The nurses in the national associations in Europe were considerably disturbed by the growth and power of the labor unions, and they felt that if the ICN opened its door to national organizations with lay members their national associations would be swamped by the leaders of labor movements. The decision was to recommend two organizations. Josephine Nelson, secretary of the committee, has described in detail the work of the committee in *New Horizons in Nursing*.[2] Hortense Hilbert who served with unusual equanimity as the chairman of the committee, through thick and thin, should be remembered with great gratitude.

The next step in the move toward structural changes after the original Structure Committee had disbanded in 1949, was the formation of a Joint Coordinating Committee on Structure. This committee consisted of the president and chairman of the Structure Committee of each of the organizations involved. The joint convention of the ANA, NOPHN, and the NLNE (1952) was the historic occasion when action took place which effected the amalgamation of four organizations to form the National League for Nursing. The NACGN had already dissolved (1951), since provision had been made in the ANA for Negro nurses to have membership, even though they could not get it through their state associations, and the American Association of Industrial Nurses had voted to retain their own organization. The National League of Nursing Education gave to Pearl McIver and me the honor of giving the addresses at the luncheon which marked the last time the NLNE met as such.

The Joint Coordinating Committee on Structure presented the structural frameworks through which at that time it seemed we could best carry out our objectives. But time proved otherwise and in 1966 the ANA and in 1967 the NLN made substantial structural changes to clarify issues and strengthen both organizations. And changes we shall have again, for the social challenges of the tomorrows always bring change.

References
1. *50th Annual Report*, NLNE. 1944, p. 50.
2. Nelson, Josephine. *New Horizons in Nursing*. The Macmillan Co., New York. 1951.

Chapter Fifteen

SUMMER INTERLUDES:
INTERNATIONAL COUNCIL OF
NURSES CONGRESSES

IN 1924, I attended my first convention of the three national nurses
organizations in Detroit. Among the speakers was a young nurse
from Finland, Kyllikki Pohjala, who was at Teachers College, and
who had come to extend an invitation to the Congress of the ICN
which was to be held in Helsingfors (or Helsinki, the Finnish name)
the next summer. It was the first congress held since before World
War I. She was a handsome, vigorous person who had served in the
Finnish-Russian War. When she told us about the work of the Finnish nurses during that war, she closed with these words: "Finland
may have lost her soil, but she has not lost her soul." Several of
us Children's Hospital graduates got to know Kyllikki Pohjala, and
four of us went to Finland to attend the Congress.

Mary Norcross and I spent some time in England before going
to Germany and Finland, and, of course, we had been entertained by
some of the British matrons who had visited the Philadelphia General
Hospital, where we were both working. We had a note of introduction
to Miss Lloyd Still (she came later to Philadelphia General) at the
Nightingale School, St. Thomas's Hospital, London. When we asked
to see the Matron, the girl in the neat frill and bow could hardly

believe that we wanted to see the Matron herself. No wonder. We learned later from Gladys Hillyers who succeeded Miss Lloyd Still as Matron, that we had been waiting on the "scrubbers' bench." When we were discovered later by an assistant Matron, we were ushered into the Matron's office, and "Matron," as she was called rather than by name, soon blustered in smiling, her hair a-flying despite the cap with the ties under the chin. She had been arranging flowers for the Nightingale Tea that afternoon and gave us a very hearty invitation to come. She showed us the Nightingale rooms and gardens, and then turned us over to the Sister Tutor who took us to the school and told us about its curriculum.

A Nightingale Tea at St. Thomas's

In the afternoon, we returned to St. Thomas's for the tea, and imagine our astonishment when on the trip there, we turned around on the bus to see Miss Derbyshire, who took us in tow. The Tea is an annual affair begun by Miss Nightingale, and all the Nightingales who are within reach return for it, along with some royal personages. First we were served tea, then ice cream and cakes and fruit cocktail, and so on. The band played, and the prominent ladies displayed their fashions.

There were about forty nurses on board the boat from Stettin, Germany, to Helsinki, and it took us two nights and one day. The captain had a special dinner for the nurses, and everybody signed each other's musical program. Among the signatures on mine is that of Sister Agnes Karll, a well-known nurse in the history of German nursing. There was a nurse from Japan, and others from Holland, Canada, Bulgaria, and Germany. Sister Agnes Karll told me that she thought nursing at that time was very impersonal. Helsinki has a beautiful harbor and there was a large delegation of nurses who escorted everyone to his lodging. One presented the card given by the committee to the customs officer, and no baggage was examined. Later, the money for the visa was returned to us.

We were taken to Mehilainen (meaning "busy bee"), a small private hospital, where we were to be guests and where we were treated with great thoughtfulness. One thing amused us. Even in this very well appointed hospital, the water from the bath seemed to run to an outside open pipe rather than into a contained drain. We packed a small bag for a weekend visit to Harjavalta, where the family of Miss Pohjala had lived on the same farm for several hundred years. We made the train by jumping on when it was moving; it took thirteen hours and thirty-seven minutes to go one hundred ninety-six miles, with all the stops made during the night. Miss Pohjala, her brother, and our two friends from Boston met us at the station. What a wild automobile ride — sixty miles an hour over narrow, unpaved roads! Our hair was down our backs when we arrived.

One of the highlights of our visit was a Finnish bath in the family sauna, a little house of two rooms in one of which was a large, field stone fireplace. The fire was built early in the day so that the stones got very hot. Over the fireplace was a balcony, the floor of which was built of slats on which we lay. The maid threw water on the hot stones and the steam rose and soon got in its work. We were served with cold drinks. Then the maid whacked us with birch twigs and leaves and gave us a soaping and washing. We descended the stairs and had buckets of cold rinsing water dashed over us. There was a lake not too far away in which we could have plunged if we had chosen to. Instead we went into the next room to be rubbed dry, massaged and powdered. We knew no such word as modesty.

A Country Festival in Finland

That evening we went to a country festival arranged in our honor. It was held on top of a hill beside a river. As we ascended the hill, we passed a line of little girls dressed in white with blue ribbons who stepped out, gave each of us a bouquet of wild flowers, and curtsied.

When we reached the meeting place, the chairman, with a blue and white sash across his chest, gave each one of us a little enameled Finnish flag stickpin, with the date engraved on the back. The master of ceremonies was Baron Emil Cedercreutz, a well-known Finnish sculptor. The band played "The Star-Spangled Banner," and we made a feeble but ineffectual attempt to sing. Baron Cedercreutz gave the address of welcome in Finnish, one of the Children's Hospital nurses responded in French, and another Finnish-American who was visiting the Pohjalas translated the speeches into English. Then there were folk dances, songs by a group of men, and a band concert. Finnish music is very sad and haunting. We had refreshments down by the river, and then we went back to the hill to watch the final dance, an old-time wedding dance in which the performers wore costumes of a hundred years before. We played games with the children, and finally wound our way home through the woods. It was as light as four o'clock at home, but our watches said twelve p.m. This meeting was on the eighteenth of July. As we went to bed, we still heard the strains of music in the distance.

The next morning we were entertained at the studio of Baron Cedercreutz, where we had a feast of good things served with the famous national drink. As we sat, the Baron cut our silhouettes and gave us a photograph of himself with one of his horses. He had a very beautiful home filled with all kinds of lovely rugs, pictures, china and antiques. In his studio, he showed us the bas-relief on which he was working. He told us that on his death he had provided that his estate should be used as a museum.

I have never seen a better-planned convention or conference. For months, the Finnish nurses had studied English so that they could have most of the proceedings in English. There was an opening musical service at which Jean Sibelius did us the honor of giving the first performance of an unpublished composition, "The Lord Is My Shepherd." Of course, besides all the meetings, there were numerous social events for all the Congress, and some special parties to which we were invited because we were friends of Kyllikki. At that time she was editor of the *Finnish Nursing Journal*. My picture got in the newspaper as a speaker at one of the round-tables. What the article said I do not know. We went to a tea given by the Chargé d'Affaires of the United States, a garden party given by the municipality of Helsinki, and a very swank affair given by the Red Cross of Finland at which Baroness and General Mannerheim received us. At that time, Baroness Mannerheim was the president of the International Council of Nurses. She was a graduate of St. Thomas's Hospital School, London. The ICN, since the Helsingfors Congress, has issued blue-and-white Congress badges, a fact which pleases the Finnish nurses, since those colors were first used by them.

Following the Congress, we went on a five-day trip by rail to the lakes. We had a special car where we spent the nights. There were about ten of us — four American nurses, Kyllikki, Baroness d'Ursell of Brussells, and some Dutch nurses. Included in this trip was a visit to a Russian monastery on an island called Valamo. We went from the mainland on a government cutter. I shall never forget the sanitary conditions, and how bravely we tried to eat the luncheon with the flies hovering about. It was simply dreadful. That afternoon, a few of us were taken to call on the Abbot of the monastery, a very neat and clean person in a spick-and-span environment. He served us cold tea and strawberries.

The church in this monastery was filled with beautiful icons studded with precious jewels. It was said that when the Russian noble ladies wanted to repent for their sins they came there and offered their jewels. On the way to Valamo, we had stopped at another island, and a choir had got aboard to sing for us the rest of the way to the monastery. One of the hymns they sang in Finnish was "Master, the Tempest Is Raging." The tempest was not raging, but there was enough rough sea for us to have seasick passengers.

A Nurse in the Finnish Cabinet

Before leaving my remembrances of Finland, I shall add some

comments on the career of my distinguished friend, Kyllikki Pohjala, for not only did she serve the nurses as the editor of their journal, but she was instrumental in promoting many measures to improve the health and welfare of the people of Finland. She was a member of the Finnish Parliament for thirty-two years during which time she introduced many health bills, and for five years she was Finland's representative in the United Nations. She was Vice Chairman of Foreign Affairs for a number of years and served in the Finnish Cabinet as Minister of Social Affairs. But she was also in a strategic position to promote world health since she served for twenty years as a member of the Interparliamentary Union which brought her into conference with the statesmen of many nations. Yet with all these responsibilities, she kept close to nursing and served several terms as one of the vice presidents of the ICN. Kyllikki Pohjala comes to this country off and on, and on her last visit it was a great pleasure to take her to New Haven to see Effie Taylor. What a joyous reunion they had!

The 1929 Congress was scheduled to convene in Peking, and some of us looked forward to a trip to China. But there was a war going on in China, and Montreal, Canada, was agreed upon. Of course, this was familiar ground and we were not very excited about going.

London, 1937

The 1933 Congress was held in two places, Paris and Brussels. I did not go, probably because there was a depression which brought many problems in nursing service. In 1937, however, Miss Norcross and I took our car over to England for the Congress in London. We had a worthwhile trip from Liverpool to London, including a stop at Goostrey, in Cheshire. We got to London too late for Queen Elizabeth's reception for the nurses and also for the trip to visit the Nightingale home at Embley Park. Again, because of the kind offices of the Matrons in London whom we had met at the Philadelphia General Hospital, Dame Lloyd Still, Miss Derbyshire, still Matron at the University Hospital, and Miss Monk, Matron of the London Hospital, we were included in most of the festivities.

We were staying at the Cowdrey Club in London where most of the Council was staying through the courtesy of Dame Lloyd Still. Among my papers at Mugar Library is a collection of Christmas cards which Dame Alicia sent me over a period of years. Some of the things pictured at St. Thomas's are no more; they were destroyed in the London blitz. On the Sunday following the Congress, Dame Alicia arranged for Gladys Hillyers, her assistant, who had spent some time with us at the Children's Hospital, to take us to Embley Park to see the Nightingale home. We also went into the little church and churchyard where Florence Nightingale is buried. The vicar was there, and he commented that Americans were more interested in Florence Nightingale than were the English.

Of course, we had all the usual gaieties of a Congress, being entertained at the Houses of Parliament and in the Great Westminster Hall, by the municipality of London and by the leading hospitals. When we went to Guy's for a garden party, a man said to us. "That's my building," and knowing it was the obstetrics building I said, "Oh! Are you chief of obstetrics there?" "Oh, no," he said, "I am the Henry Ford of England. I gave that building. I am Lord So and So."

Since we had our car and were going up into Scotland and around England and into Wales, we invited Effie Taylor, who had just been made the President of the ICN, and Susan Francis, the President of ANA, to go with us. We had a wonderful time. There is only one event of that trip which deserves mention here. We were going through a town in Derbyshire, and the guidebook mentioned quite casually that Lea Hurst, the home of Florence Nightingale, was nearby. It meant going off our course a bit, and the chauffeur demurred since she wanted to get settled for the night, but the courier, who happened to be me, finally persuaded her. When we reached the village of Belper, we asked a nice "bobby" for directions. We were told to go up a hill and find a white gate. We went up several hills and down roundabout, but no white gate. Finally, we stopped a bicyclist who started us on our way again. We were going by a rather insignificant gray gate when we heard him shout that that was the place.

A Visit to Lea Hurst

All we had hoped for was a glimpse of the house from the road, but the guardian angel that took care of us all through the journey took care of us then, for here was a sign saying the gardens were open for the benefit of some local charity. A winding road led down over the hillside to the house which overlooks the valley and the hills. It was to Lea Hurst that Florence Nightingale went on her return from the Crimea, and it was of this house that she wrote, "If ever I live to see England again, the western breezes of my hilltop home will be my first longing." There was a funny little old man at the door to collect shillings. We were directed into a room in which there was a collection of Nightingale treasures, among them a knee desk that the soldiers had given Miss Nightingale and a set of cutlery which she had used most of her life which was a gift from the workmen in Sheffield. The walls were covered with photographs of her at all ages.

When the lady who was acting as hostess saw our great interest in the collection, she realized that we were American nurses and arranged for us to meet Mr. L. H. Shore Nightingale, who then occupied the house and was a first cousin of Miss Nightingale. From that moment on, we were his personal guests. He took us through the house, showed us the day and night nurseries, the room Miss Nightingale occupied as she grew older, and the cat's palace. Miss Nightingale's bedroom was then Mr. Nightingale's, and over his bed was a photograph which he said looked just like her when she was "giving you a poser." Some of the nursery furniture made from oaks on the estate was still in the nursery, as were some of Miss Nightingale's treasures of childhood and girlhood.

In one of the hallways was a cabinet which housed a collection of shells which Miss Nightingale had made. They were arranged in black-velvet-lined drawers, and each little card bearing the shell told of the habitat of the crustacean printed in a firm hand by Miss Nightingale. We went out on the balcony outside the night nursery and looked over the gardens, the rolling countryside, and the Derwent River. While in Scutari, Miss Nightingale had written of the sound of the Straits, "How I like to hear that ceaseless roar; it puts me in mind of the dear Derwent; how often I have listened to it from the nursery window." And here we were, listening to it from that same nursery window.

We had tea in the old family dining-room with Mr. Nightingale and Miss MacLean, his hostess, and such a tea! They told us about the road to take from there through the Duke of Devonshire's estate and about places to stop in Scotland. We were invited to sign Mr. Nightingale's guest book. When we left, they came out to the car to speed us on our way and sent us out by another gate so that we could drive through the estate.

The next ICN Congress was in Atlantic City in 1947, a lapse of ten years since the previous one. World War II had intervened. In the meantime, Effie Taylor had kept the ICN together. I was ill at the time, so I missed that Congress. It was a great disappointment not to greet some of my friends from abroad, and I had looked forward also to seeing Lavinia Dock for the first time. She was to receive an ICN award. Although Miss Dock gave up her nursing activities in this country to devote her time and energy to the suffrage movement, she had retained the secretaryship of the ICN. She was its first secretary and served until 1922. She gloried in her role as a militant suffragist.

But we did go to Rome in 1957. Of course I was then retired and out on the sidelines, but I was interested in being able to see many of the people whom I had known over the years. I was flattered when I was introduced to a young native Philippine nun, who with some excitement in her voice said, "Oh, I learn about you in history of nursing." It was a stirring occasion when new countries were admitted into membership, and at the Rome Congress several nursing associations from black countries were admitted. Their representatives wore very colorful costumes. That was my last ICN Congress.

After one has read the foregoing about the International Council of Nursing, she or he (for I have some good friends among male nurses) may well say that nothing was said about the work of the International Council or what took place at meetings. This is as I meant it to be. All business transactions at these meetings took place at the closed meetings of the Council on which served representatives from each country having membership, and at meetings of its committees. The meetings for others at the Congress were program meetings, not much different from what one would expect at any convention. The International Council of Nurses has within the last year or two published a history by Daisy Bridges, its secretary for many years. What I tried to convey in this chapter was the generous hospitality of the host country, and the opportunities afforded to meet with nurses from many lands and to enjoy friendly fellowship with them.

Chapter Sixteen

OBSERVATIONS FROM THE PERIPHERY

I T was a great joy to be able to attend the 1967 convention of the National League for Nursing for many reasons, chief of which was the satisfaction of seeing old friends. But that year there were three other paramount reasons for going. First, during the convention week, the Teachers College Alumnae dinner was to be held at which I was to be the recipient of the R. Louise McManus Award; second, I had agreed to give a paper at the meeting sponsored by the Committee on Historical Source Materials in Nursing; and third, there were rumors of "fireworks" at the convention, and this was an innovation at a League meeting.

It will be recalled that at the 1965 League convention, the membership had passed a resolution known as Resolution 5 which called for an orderly movement of nursing education into institutions of higher education, "in such a way that the flow of nurses into the community will not be interrupted." Then came the bombshell with the publication, in December, 1965, of the ANA *Position Paper*, which not only stated that "Education for all those who are licensed to practice nursing should take place in institutions of higher education," but also recommended that there be only two classifications of nurses, professional nurses to be prepared in baccalaureate programs, and technical nurses to be prepared in associate degree programs. There were also to be aides.[1] The paper had been pre-

[151]

pared by the Committee on Education of the ANA and passed by the Board of Directors. It had not been placed before the membership of the organization when it was made public. In my opinion, the issuance of the position paper was badly timed, and had it been accompanied by the excellent joint statement of the ANA and NLN in regard to community planning which followed, as well as a statement of assurance to present practitioners regarding their status, it is possible that there would have been less unrest and ferment. Then came an outcry from the AHA, supported by many League members, especially those in positions in hospital schools of nursing, that Resolution 5 should be rescinded at the 1967 convention. In anticipation of the convention, meetings were being held in various parts of the country by hospital schools, and backed by local AHA members. At the convention, it was evident that the AHA had marshalled its forces. The air was electrified. For the meeting at which the vote on the rescinding of Resolution 5 was scheduled, bus-loads of people arrived. In all my years of attendance at conventions of the NLNE and NLN, never have I been at one where there was the tenseness in the atmosphere which prevailed at this meeting.

I was against rescinding the motion, because I believe in the principle for which it stands, and also I do not believe that one association should force the members of another group against the wall to rescind a vote. I was reminded again and again of the situation which we had when we first began our work in accreditation. In 1967, as a member of the League, and as an older member of the profession who had been active in trying to promote better standards of nursing education, I wanted to speak my piece. When the motion was made to rescind Resolution 5, members could not get to the many microphones scattered throughout the room quickly enough to express their views. There were queues behind each microphone. Some persons spoke well and to the point, others emotionally and illogically. I was sitting at the side of the auditorium and finally my turn came at the microphone. There was no recognition by the chairman, and in my opinion she adjourned the meeting rather precipitately. I could not stay on for the adjourned meeting the next day, but was determined that if there was a way to have my piece said I would find it. I called the president and asked if it were within parliamentary procedure to have a statement from me read by another member of the organization. She assured me that it was, and Martha Rogers read the statement which I hastily prepared.[2] It expressed my opposition to the rescinding of Resolution 5 and my reasons for supporting it. Miss Haynes, the general director of NLN wrote me a note shortly after the meeting thanking me for expressing my views as an older member of the profession. Resolution 5 was not rescinded. There appears to have been plenty of activity following the convention, and the issue of whether hospital schools shall be continued indefinitely is not yet settled, nor will it be, probably, for some time to come.

To my knowledge, the ANA has made few significant educational pronouncements in its history. The reason for this is that there was an organization whose chief concern was nursing education, the NLNE, and the ANA had recognized its role as such. Until the 'thirties, most of the membership in the ANA came from the private duty field, and its members were concerned with their problems as practitioners. When its education committee issued a position paper in December, 1965, the implications had more impact than usual. There is nothing new about the position stated by the ANA in relation to the professional nurse. What is new is that it came as an official pronouncement from a professional organization. It had been stated long ago by many of our educators, from Miss Nutting on, that the professional nurse should be educated within a university.

The Development of University Schools

A few remarks here may be appropriate about the growth and development of collegiate schools of nursing, for they too have changed, especially in the last decade.

At the beginning of this century, there was not a collegiate or university school of nursing in the world. By the end of the first third of the century, there were roughly three dozen schools with a basic program leading to the baccalaureate degree. During the 'forties, the number of degree programs increased greatly, but here is the rub: many of them could not qualify for membership in the Association of Collegiate Schools of Nursing, to say nothing of meeting the present concept of a degree program. There were only sixteen collegiate schools in 1946 that were full members of the ACSN and in 1952, only forty-five out of 117 programs were fully accredited by the National Accrediting Service.[3]

I have the temerity to say that some hospital schools in the 'thirties and 'forties had sounder educational standards for nursing education than did some of the collegiate programs in mediocre colleges which had no provision for liberal education and nursing education to complement each other, and whose clinical facilities and teaching staffs were inadequate. Nursing education and nursing were not very well understood by many university officials, and during the depression in the 'thirties and in the war years, some of them found a nursing school one way of increasing the university population. The early schools were organized as departments of the medical schools. Later, there were some within departments of household economics or education.

One study in the late 'twenties showed only three collegiate or university schools that were autonomous units within the university.[4] In the late 'forties, I heard a president of a university that had a school of nursing refer to nurses as "the handmaids of physicians." When I challenged him, he said that "handmaid" was a perfectly good word, and quoted the biblical reference to the "handmaid of the Lord." My retort was that a physician is not the Lord. This same university president later became an outstanding exponent of sound university education for nurses.

Not too long ago, I noticed an announcement by the Health Administrator of New York City that registered nurses would be appointed to the Medical Board of the Municipal Hospitals, and he added, "New York nurses are going to be professionals; they will no longer be doctors' handmaidens but will be professional partners." So you see that the old idea was still hanging on in the present decade.

The demands now being made on nurses will increase as breakthroughs occur in medical science, and as new goals and reappraisals in health services to a growing population are projected. There will be new roles for professional nurses that will demand the broad kind of preparation given in a university school.

The Pain of Transition

I have lived through many progressive changes in nursing education, and each time change was initiated, we had the shouting and the tumult. However, it would be disastrous if hospitals and other agencies closed their schools prematurely. I am not too sure that we should have only two groups of nurses. Where would the hospital nursing services be today without the licensed practical nurse? But if they are retained, their education should be given within the general system of education. Frankly, the word "technical" disturbs me. One of my hopes is that in university or any other preparation for nursing it will be possible to give students sufficient practice in clinical procedures so that they are at ease in using the essential skills and at the same time can establish good communication with their patients. Both are necessary. Sometimes there is the communication, but the patient is concerned about the skill with which procedure is carried out. There cannot be nursing in the fullness of what it should be without both skill and interaction between the patient and the nurse.

We hear too often that "nursing today is not what it used to be," and it usually is meant to imply that it is not as good. I challenge that from my own experience as a patient. It all depends on one's concept of nursing. If it is to lie in bed and expect glorified, luxury maid service, then nursing is not what it used to be. But if it is intelligent care backed by knowledge of the "why and wherefore" of the existing condition when one is critically ill, then it is what it used to be and sometimes better, provided one is in a hospital which fulfills its avowed purpose — to furnish good medical and nursing care to its patients.

In the painful transition that nursing must go through, I have faith that there are leaders who have a high regard for the health and welfare of human beings, and who will not discard the old values which are worthy of being retained. Certainly, there are levels of nursing needs which require different levels of preparation, but unless education at whatever level fosters in the person the understanding and sensitivity that makes her compassionately identify herself with the needs of those whom she serves, the rest is like sounding brass and tinkling cymbals.

Setting standards of education and practice, and providing for economic security is an inherent right of any professional organization, and this right calls for professional unity to support it. At the same time, nursing is a strong social force and cannot be separated from the culture of which it is a part. Here we have a ground of value for having representatives of allied professional groups, educators, and community leaders thinking, planning, and acting together with nurses to meet community needs in nursing education and service. There are nurses today who have difficulty in accepting the concept that changes which profoundly affect society and professions within that society do not take place at a particular moment in a small fraction of chronological time. Nor can there be a *precise* timetable. But that does not imply that we should lag. Whenever we find valid grounds for change, it is our responsibility to move into action, and that action should proceed as rapidly as the resources of a given community make it possible and practicable.

Time in the abstract creates neither challenge nor change. It is what is happening in the social order at certain periods of time that moves individuals to offer challenges for change and to move into action. Social and cultural settings are not permanent backdrops; they are dynamic, changing scenes within which nursing plays its role. The sets change with the times, and nurses must adjust themselves to the new order, both in education and in service, if they are to give the quality and kinds of services that people need. We have come a long way up the hill of education. We have overcome many odds, and though we have not always agreed as to ways and means, let us not forget that there was a sizable number of trustees, administrators of hospitals, and physicians, who lent their support to the upgrading of nursing education. I think it was James Thurber who wrote: "Let us not look backward in anger, nor forward in fear, but around us in awareness."

References

1. *A Position Paper*. American Nurses' Association, 1965, p. 5.
2. Goostray, Stella. Personal Memorandum, May, 1967.
3. Roberts, Mary M. *American Nursing*. The Macmillan Company, New York. 1954, p. 521.
4. "Report of University Relations Committee." *33rd Annual Report*. NLNE. 1927, p. 52.

Chapter Seventeen

MAINLY ABOUT FRIENDS

I T is an honor to hold the office of president in a national professional organization. I know of only one person in the League who openly campaigned for the honor. When news of her politicking reached the convention *via* members of her own state league, a statement was offered at a meeting which subtly but firmly decried the practice. The person involved was not elected, and I doubt if she ever forgave some of us for airing it in the convention. Henceforth, she had little to do with the League. The names of persons who have agreed to serve if elected are usually suggested to the nominating committee by the state organizations. I believe that acceptance of this office, or any other office, is motivated by the candidate's belief that her peers thought she had something to give to the organization and should be willing to serve.

The honor demands commitment of time and energy, and the will to face choices and to make decisions. One of the sidelines of a national officer, or even of a state officer, is to give addresses on all sorts of occasions. Of speech-making there would be no end if one accepted all the invitations. I gave many speeches, but the number was curtailed by the fact that during my term as president of the League, we were in a time of national emergency.

Invitations to give addresses at graduation exercises were numerous, and during the 'thirties especially, when I was secretary of the

League, I accepted many of them because, as a director of a school, I felt sorry for some of the directors of the smaller schools who usually had to turn to members of the medical staff. I remember vividly one graduation at the Children's — not my own, nor when I was director of the school — when the chief of the medical staff gave a paternalistic address which included these words: "If a family doesn't pay your bill, sue them." Such inspiring words for the new graduate!

At first, I conscientiously wrote an address for each school calculated to air some views on nursing education and to give a modicum of professional advice to new graduates. Who cared what I said? Student and parent alike were waiting for the moment when the name "Mary Elizabeth Smith" was called and there was a new graduate nurse. I recall one address in which I had very carefully included some things that I wanted the president of the Board of Trustees to hear, for he was anything but a friend of nursing education. After my address, the president called for a "few words" from a former director of the nursing service and school who was visiting in the town. She proceeded to give a long speech which I think helped the president to salve his conscience about attacks on nursing education. She should have known better, for she was prominent in the affairs of the ANA and secretary of a state board in the Middle West. Eventually, I began to gain wisdom about graduation addresses and worked out a few woven around the theme, Which Shall it be — In the Profession or Of it, to which I could add material to fit the school I was addressing. That was my "pork barrel."

But the occasions provided some interesting views of local practices, ranging from simple, dignified ceremonials to others that were amusing to me. At one school I had to walk down the aisle between two lines of the graduates and under the crossed diplomas. One time I was addressing one of the larger Boston schools, whose exercises were held in a large church. I was speaking from the pulpit when suddenly I saw movement in the main aisle! A mouse was being chased by a cat! Not being partial to either of the critters, I was afraid that the mouse would reach the pulpit and take refuge under my long skirt. But cat and mouse took a detour, much to my relief.

Once a rather embarrassing situation developed. I stood at the reading desk and began my address. Before many minutes, I began to sneeze, and my eyes began to water. The beautiful bouquet in front of me evidently had some pollen to which I was allergic. My bag, containing my handkerchief, was on my chair and I turned to get it, at which point the minister realized my plight and brought the bag to me. He then removed the bouquet.

The Pioneers

But holding office as an officer or as a member of a board of directors, especially on the national level, had many compensations. There were opportunities to meet with educators in the field of general education, to attend conferences, and in many ways, to broaden one's knowledge and professional outlook. To me, however, one of the rewarding compensations was that I came to know some of the great women of our profession.

In her *American Nursing*, Mary Roberts commented that the age of the great nurse pioneers was passing into history.[1] She was referring to the mid-'twenties. It was my good fortune to become involved in national nursing activities in the mid-'twenties. If one looks back in nursing history, no outstanding figures emerge until the late 'eighties, save for Linda Richards. There were few schools and no bond between them. But in some of those schools were the women who would participate in the great pioneer work fifteen to twenty years later. They were mature women, many of them former teachers who had entered these schools.

Three women stand out in the 'nineties. They were Isabel Hampton (later Mrs. Robb), Lavinia L. Dock, and Mary Adelaide Nutting, forceful personalities with creative, analytic minds, and with drive and talent to work out their plans. This small group and those who were associated with them believed that nursing was an essential social service, capable of becoming a strong social force as it developed its professional responsibility. The time had come for them to refute the growing idea that the main purpose of a training school was to supply nursing service to the hospital as cheaply as possible. That small group, without precedent to guide them, set about to define a sound educational philosophy and create the means to achieve it. They recognized that the first step was to organize an association whose chief concern was the education of student nurses. Then should follow an organization concerned with the nurse as a practitioner. The third step in the pioneer development was the launching of a professional journal. Of the pioneers, I knew only two, Adelaide Nutting, nurse educator, and Mary M. Riddle, active in the promotion of the *American Journal of Nursing,* and the third president of the Associated Alumnae.

I heard Lillian Wald speak many times, but I never knew her personally. The last time I saw her was in one of the old brass shops on Allen Street in New York, where she appeared to be driving a good bargain with the owner. Although I wrote a biographical profile of Mary Adelaide Nutting for the one-hundredth anniversary of her birth,[2] I like best to recall two visits with Miss Nutting which stand out vividly in my memory. One was in the early 'thirties. She had telephoned from Groton, Massachusetts, and asked me to meet her at the North Station, since she had several hours to wait for another train to Maine. Her first topic of conversation as we sat in the station was a job opening for me which I did not want. After that little matter was settled, most of her conversation was about professional literature and the need of the profession to have a larger supply and of better quality. She regarded professional magazines as vital to the development of nursing. She specifically mentioned as one of our needs a journal devoted to research in nursing in which results of studies could be reported. She would rejoice that the profession has such a publication in *Nursing Research* even if it did take until 1952 to get it. The will and the writing potential were there much earlier, but as usual it was lack of money that was the deterring factor. Another subject about which she seemed greatly concerned was the need for professional nurses to come to the defense of others who were being unjustly treated. An incident had occurred in a large school in the Middle West where the director of the school had suspended a student for infringement of a rule which had been made by the family who supported the hospital. The student went to a member of the family, and the director was ordered to reinstate her. The episode ended in the forced (I believe) resignation of the director. Miss Nutting thought that the *American Journal of Nursing* should have given publicity to the incident, and that the profession should have rallied to the support of the director.

The other visit took place when I presented the first Nutting Award to Mary Adelaide Nutting in her apartment in the spring of 1944. (Little did I think that one day one of those medals would be mine.) Isabel Stewart, Anna Wolf and Miss Nutting's companion were the only others present. Miss Nutting's memory had begun to fail somewhat, but not about her early days at Johns Hopkins and her associations with Isabel Hampton, who it seemed ranked next to Florence Nightingale in her esteem. Nor did she forget to question Anna Wolf about progress toward a university school at Johns Hopkins.

When I knew Miss Riddle, she was the superintendent of nurses and of the training school at the Newton Cottage Hospital, now the Newton-Wellesley Hospital, in Newton, Massachusetts. She was one of the examiners when I took the Massachusetts State Board Examination. We had a written examination one day and returned the next day for a "practical examination" which consisted of identifying five or six articles. One of the articles I had to identify was several feet of flexible rubber tubing. For the life of me I could not remember its name. I said, "I can tell you what it is used for but I can't recall what it is called." "All right," said she, "tell me what is is used for." When I had finished she quietly said "tourniquet." That type of practical examination was a farce and was discarded by Massachusetts in the 'thirties. I had the pleasure of helping to throw it into the discard.

The Disciples Carry On

In the first fifteen years of the new century, there appeared a larger group of women to carry on the work begun by those few pioneers. They, too, were well-equipped with education, creative skill, and talent. Some of them were still active in the national organizations when I became a member of a board, and it was my good fortune to know them and serve with them on committees. In this group were Annie W. Goodrich, Mary S. Gardner, Isabel Stewart, Laura Logan, Effie Taylor, Julia Stimson, Elizabeth Burgess, Lillian Clayton, and Mary Beard. Of the group I have named, only Effie Taylor and Laura Logan are living.

Effie Taylor's influence was felt not only in national but in international affairs. It was she who held together the ICN during World War II by means of her frequent letters to those colleagues in foreign countries who could be reached. And long after her retirement as the second dean of the Yale School of Nursing, she kept closely in touch with national nursing affairs and has been a wise counselor to nurses in Connecticut.

It was Laura Logan who planned and offered the first five-year program in nursing leading to a baccalaureate degree. This was at the University of Cincinnati.

Isabel Stewart, who probably influenced my nursing career more than any other one person, I have also portrayed in a biographical profile,[4] and I believe others of this group have been mentioned in other chapters of these memoirs. They were all women whom I admired and recognized as leaders in solving present problems and building for the future.

Annie Goodrich was one of the most colorful personalities in nursing history. As I have indicated previously, she was a very formidable foe when she battled for a cause, but she was a delightful person to meet socially, and she wrote charming letters.[5] A little episode I recall with a smile was the occasion when I was with a group at the Yale School of Nursing who were being "taken on a tour." We were waiting outside the dean's office, and I heard Miss Goodrich say, when an assistant told her I was in the group, "Pick out a nice-looking student to take Miss Goostray around." She referred to the fact that someone had said to me once, "You have such nice-looking students at the Children's," and I replied facetiously, "Yes, I pick them for their looks." I never lived it down.

One of the most gracious of the leaders in those days was Mary Sewell Gardner, who helped to make 1912 an historic year in American nursing, for in that year, the National Organization for Public Health Nursing was established. Forty years later, on another historic occasion, Mary Gardner was present when the NOPHN dissolved and merged into the National League for Nursing. Following that 1952 convention, Mary Gardner wrote me a note thanking me for helping to bring about the new organization. So much did I value that letter, it is among my papers in the Nursing Archive, Mugar Library, Boston.[6]

The next group to come along was that with which I was associated, women in my age group, plus or minus a few years: Sophie Nelson, whom I called a "public health statesman," Alma Haupt, Anna Wolf, Nellie Hawkinson, Claribel Wheeler, Blanche Pfefferkorn, Marian Rottman (Fleming), and Sister Olivia, to name only a few. And in the middle 'thirties, the names of Anne L. Austin, whose work as a historian and researcher in nursing is well-known, Ruth Sleeper, Lucile Petry, and Marion Sheahan become more closely identified with national affairs, but they belonged to a younger age group.

Active at this time also was a group of women, most of whom also were younger than we, who were at the Vassar Training Camp in World War I days. They were well-educated women, in the full meaning of the term, some of whom had given up other professions when they entered nursing. Most of them were in public health nursing, and I suspect it was because they felt they would have a better opportunity to initiate action and use their creative talents in that field than they would have in established institutions. The Vassar group was augmented by other women of similar preparation who had not attended the Vassar Camp. These women brought to nursing a realistic approach to problems and a broad concept of nursing in a new social age. They were good for us.

Sometimes we are to apt to regard as leaders only the articulate ones whose voices may be heard, as it were, from the house tops. But never underestimate the leadership of women who are on boards and committees, and quietly but forcefully exert a powerful influence. They are the ones who listen and at the crucial moment ask a telling question which compels people to concentrate on the real issues. We have had many such women whose influence has not been recognized.

Naturally, the women I knew best were my associates on the League Board, because we worked very closely together and established an enduring relationship which has gone on through the years. I have been on many boards, but I can think of none whose members worked more harmoniously. There were never any bitter entanglements, though we did not always agree.

The meetings of the Joint Boards gave us opportunities to know the members of the other national boards, and we worked together on joint projects. I recall with great pleasure some of the non-nurse members of the NOPHN board, and also the opportunity afforded to us, especially through the National Council for War Service to meet and be entertained by persons like Miss Mabel Boardman, the devoted secretary of the American Red Cross Nursing Service, and Mrs. Walter Lippman, who did such a magnificent job with Red Cross Aides during World War II.

Incidental mention has been made of Mary Beard in various connections, but she deserves better than this for her work not only in World War II but also in World War I. She was chairman of the Subcommittee on Public Health Nursing of the government's Council of National Defense and directed the effective use of public health nurses in the civilian community. My first personal remembrance of Mary Beard was when I was a senior student reluctantly going to public health lectures — reluctantly because we had to give up a few evenings for them. At one lecture, she told us about the work of the Instructive Visiting Nurse Association of Boston. She was its director. She also gave one of the graduation addresses at the Children's while I was a student. Strangely enough, I remember that she quoted Christina Rossetti's poem, "Does the Road Wind Uphill All the Way?"

Miss Beard was the wartime president of the NOPHN (1916-1919). In 1924, she went to the Rockefeller Foundation and sent a number of foreign students to the Philadelphia General while I was there. But I got to know her well when she arranged for Thai students to come to the Children's Hospital. In 1938, Mary Beard became the director of the American Red Cross Nursing Service, and there began for her a period of strenuous and anxious years during which she gave statesmanlike service. In my contacts with her when we had the Thai students, I found her to be understanding and helpful, but even more so did I find these qualities when I was president of the National Nursing Council for War Service and we were involved together in situations which might be termed "ticklish." The tensions and anxieties of war problems took their toll of Mary Beard, and she resigned as director of the Red Cross Nursing Service in 1944. She died two years later.

Her resignation came at a crucial time for us all, but fortunately she had as her associate a young woman, quiet but forceful, who took over the directorship. She was Virginia Dunbar, one of those leaders who remain in the background. Nevertheless, she carried on some important assignments as Miss Beard's associate both in this country and abroad. Miss Dunbar remained with the Red Cross to the end of the war.

Although I never served as an officer of the ANA, I always felt a responsibility to serve on any committee of the organization on which I was invited to serve, both on the national and on the state level. I was once asked by one of the large state associations (not my own) to allow it to suggest my name for the ANA presidency (with the backing of two other state associations) but at the time I was too much involved in NLNE affairs, and I declined. It would have been a challenging job had I accepted and been elected.

In 1927, Mary Norcross and I built a small house in Blue Hill, Maine, and here we welcomed many of our friends in nursing. It is a matter of much regret that we did not keep a guest-book, for many friends who have played significant parts in the nursing profession in these United States have been guests. Some came as house guests, others unexpectedly dropped in to call or to have a meal with us. Imagine my surprise one late afternoon in the early 'thirties when a car stopped at the driveway and there were Mary Adelaide Nutting and Harriet Bailey. Miss Nutting was spending the summer in Castine. I had not known she was there, or I would have gone to call on her. She found me in a carpenter's apron shingling part of the back of the house, my stocking torn from knee to ankle. When I showed her my "study" on a corner of the lot, which I called "Independence Hall," she said, "You will never get any work done there. The view is much too nice."

One of my nieces has never forgotten the day Julia Stimson came to lunch. She had been to St. Andrews, New Brunswick, and wrote that on her way back she would like to stop and have lunch with us. After lunch, my niece, who was about twelve, was sitting at one end of a heavy wooden settle. Julia went over to show "what the man did" when he came to start her electric refrigerator which had refused to operate. She grabbed the end of the settle on which my niece was sitting, lifted it and niece about six inches, and then let them drop. In the time between the lifting and the dropping Margaret found herself at the opposite end of the settle.

Recently I found an old notebook which somehow escaped the fire we had some fifteen years ago in which I had noted the names of some of our guests. It reads like a *Who's Who in Nursing*, and few names of the people with whom I was closely associated are absent. Isabel Stewart did not get to Blue Hill, nor did Lillian Clayton after the house was built, but she had seen the site and begged us not to disturb the wild roses. A bush is still at our kitchen door.

References

1. Roberts, Mary M. *American Nursing*. The Macmillan Company, New York. 1954.
2. Goostray, Stella. "Mary Adelaide Nutting." *American Journal of Nursing*. November, 1958.
3. Citation, Mary Adelaide Nutting Award to Stella Goostray, 1955.

4. Goostray, Stella. "Isabel M. Stewart." *American Journal of Nursing*. March, 1954.
5. Letter, Annie W. Goodrich to Stella Goostray, June 28, 1943.
6. Letter, Mary S. Gardner to Stella Goostray. July 5, 1953.
7. Goostray, Stella. "Sophie Nelson: Public Health Statesman." *American Journal of Nursing*. September, 1960.

Chapter Eighteen

NURSING AS A CONTINUING SOCIAL FORCE

MY interest in historical writing and in the preservation of historical source materials was stimulated at Teachers College. From then on, I collected historical material, some of which was given to the Mary Adelaide Nutting Collection. Browsing around in old book shops was an interesting pastime, especially the shops on Old Cornhill in Boston. A fortunate find for me was an advertisement in a national magazine in which a gentleman whose family had been connected with one of the old magazines published in New York said he was clearing out his attic and had clippings from old magazines on every conceivable subject. So I sounded him out on nursing. Sure enough he had some. He sent me quite a number of articles about Florence Nightingale written while she was still in the Crimea. These and other articles came from time to time, some of them marked "rare," and the price was anywhere from a quarter to half-a-dollar. Once when he was in London he sent several articles from the *London Times,* including a page with the well-known drawing of Florence Nightingale going among the wounded with a lantern in her hand, and also one with her famous coach. Evidently he could not remember my name but did remember the address, Children's Hospital, Boston. The letter was addressed to "Miss Nosegay." Incidentally, let it be recorded here that my name is Stella Goostray — no middle initial.

Someone conferred an "M" on me about twenty years ago, and it keeps cropping up. It has even been engraved on a plaque!

To get back to my interest in history, Isabel Stewart organized a Committee on Early Source Materials in 1948, with three members. In addition to Isabel Stewart, there were Helen W. Munson and I. That Committee has developed into the representative Committee on Historical Source Materials in Nursing of the National League for Nursing. A history of that committee will be found in the article "Nation-wide Hunt for Nursing's Historical Treasures."[1] Membership on that early committee was my undoing as far as nursing history is concerned, because I became a history buff.

Nursing is an essential social service, and its history should be studied within the context of social history. The profession should make available to social historians source materials which will indicate the contribution of nursing to the social and cultural development of this country. The Committee on Historical Source Materials in Nursing was greatly elated when it found that the biographical dictionary on *Notable American Women, 1607-1950*, sponsored by Radcliffe College will include a group of Civil War nurses and a sizable group of professional nurses. It seemed to the committee that a new vein in the mine of social history had been opened by the inclusion of nursing. Several members of our committee were invited to prepare some of these biographical profiles. Later I was invited to be on the Advisory Committee of the biographical dictionary and, still later, on the Advisory Committee of the Elizabeth and Arthur Schlesinger Library on the History of Women in America, formerly known as the Women's Archives of Radcliffe College. It is to me further evidence that nursing history is being recognized as part of the country's social history.

Having said *mea culpa* because of source materials which I discarded, I plead with today's nurses to save contemporary material and to search out material from the past. Historians of the future will use contemporary sources in their history of those significant events in nursing which are taking place now. It is only if individuals record nursing history as it happens that we shall have valuable and valid source materials not only for future social historians but for nurse historians. Few will disagree about the importance of some of the events now taking place, like the study of schools being made by an independent committee, the campaign being waged by the American Nurses' Association to have all nursing education in educational institutions, and the equally vigorous campaign of the American Hospital Association to retain hospital schools.

Search Out Source Material

Some years ago, after the death of a well-known nurse who had given leadership to nursing especially in the field of public health, some of her colleagues approached her sister to ask for her papers for preservation in nursing archives. The papers had been burned the previous day. A nurse who was writing a biographical sketch of this particular nurse for *Notable American Women* had a most difficult time locating the authentic place of her birth. She hardly could have been born in three places, but the author had found three places mentioned as her birthplace.

The writer remembers her indignation when she discovered on top of the trash pile at the Children's Hospital a picture of the first Lady Superintendent (the title by which she was designated) of the hospital and a scrapbook which had been thrown out in the housecleaning of a storage place. Some months later, Ann Doyle, who was writing a series of historical biographical articles for the *American Journal of Nursing* on Sisters and Deaconesses who served in the Civil War and in the years following, told me that she was stymied in her search for information about a Civil War nurse, and the only person who seemed to know about her was a Baltimore clergyman who died suddenly the day before Miss Doyle was to have had an interview with him.

Miss Doyle came to Boston to get information about the Sisters of St. Margaret (Episcopal) and their connection with the hospital. I asked her the name of the nurse, and she said, "Adeline Tyler." I went to my office closet, brought out the picture and the scrapbook I had rescued and said, "This is Adeline Tyler, the first Lady Superintendent of the Children's Hospital, and this scrapbook has considerable information about her." Mrs. Tyler is one of the Civil War nurses included in *Notable American Women*. To prevent the loss of such material as I have cited, we need nurses on the alert for source materials.

We have had a spate of histories of nursing published during the past few years. It is unfortunate that sometimes authors have not gone to source materials for documentation for some of the statements they make. The errors are not always serious, but they do perpetuate incorrect information. There needs to be better proofreading also, for one may find a date on one page and a different date somewhere along in the book for the same event. It is not always easy to avoid errors, as I well know, and having prepared these memoirs I may find myself still further in the position of a pot calling the kettle black!

Some current historians of nursing seem to use titles not in use at the time of which they are writing: for example, "director," for a person in charge of a school, and "school of nursing." Why not use the titles in use at the time, "superintendent" and "training school," since they give some indication of the concept of professional nursing education current at the time?

One of the pitfalls of authors of biographical material is that of enlarging upon the achievement of the person about whom they are writing. For example, not too many years ago an obituary of a leading nurse educator appeared in one of our professional magazines. The statement was made that she wrote the 1927 *Curriculum for Schools of Nursing*. That curriculum was the work of many individuals under the leadership of Isabel Stewart. The person who was named as its author was a member of the Education Committee and participated as did the other members. The same account also contained the statement that the person established the first baccalaureate degree program. Had the author added the area of the country where it was established, the statement would have been correct.

These instances are cited because they show how careful admirers should be to check before submitting information for publication. The person in question had made enough significant contributions to nursing education and to other aspects of nursing to establish her place in American nursing, and she did not need these embellishments. It did seem to me that the editor ought to have known that no one person writes a curriculum and also should have been sufficiently conversant with the history of baccalaureate programs to know that quite a number had been established prior to this. However, it was an excellent program with a progressive and sound philosophy of university education for nursing that was established in this case.

It is encouraging that there is a growing number of graduate students in our universities who are interested in historical research studies of the events and personalities that have shaped nursing in this country, because nursing in this country has had, and will continue to have, a dynamic and exciting history. Its story needs to be told, and it ought to be told accurately.

Reference

1. Goostray, Stella. "Nation-Wide Hunt for Nursing's Historical Treasures." *Nursing Outlook.* January, 1965, p. 26. Reprint distributed by NLN.

L'ENVOI

Now the shadows lengthen and time grows short. As I look back, there are no regrets that I changed my vocation, for my commitment to nursing has provided intellectual stimulus and rewarding opportunities to contribute to the profession's literature, as well as to help guide young people — even "angry young women," for we had some in my day — toward maturity. There have also been the great personal satisfactions of participating in a service essential to meeting the health needs of people, and of having the joy of enduring and enriching friendships. Neither am I sorry that I received my nursing education at the Children's Hospital. I am proud of the important contributions which graduates of the Children's Hospital School of Nursing have made to the profession and also of the important contributions which the many graduates of this school are making in their communities through health and welfare activities.

So the record stands. Let it be "examined in love," in the words of St. John of the Cross, an old Spanish Saint, and let it be judged on whatever merit it has.

OLD SHINGLES

These old shingles, gray with age,
For one-score years
Have felt the gentle touch of rain drops,
The heavy snows, the melting sun,
They have guarded well those who dwelt beneath them.
Men say they have outlived their usefulness;
Yet now discarded, they kindle flame
To warm the aged,
And give ashes for new life in the garden.

S. G., October, 1949

AUTUMN

The summer's gone, and the early frost
    Whitens the field at the break of day.
The sumac flames in the noon-tide sun
    Like tongues of fire. Shadows come early.

Gray ledges are splashed with copper and bronze.
    The marsh is brown from the searing grass;
But the poplars shimmer like golden lace,
    As they dance to the pipes of the wind.

The blueberry patch has changed her dress
    From blue of the sky to crimson red.
The swamp maple flaunts her scarlet hues,
    'Gainst the pine's dark green. She is not shy.

These are the signs of an aging year
    That all men see. But do they know
That deep within, like sacramental grace,
    There waits the new life of the spring?

S. G., October, 1954

Epilogue

Stella Goostray had an avid interest in history. She was one of the three original members of the National League for Nursing Education Committee on Early Nursing Source Materials, 1949. From 1952 through 1964 she served as regional consultant, North Atlantic Area, National League for Nursing Committee on Historical Source Materials in Nursing. Earlier she had published articles urging nursing to save its treasures. From the beginning Miss Goostray was a staunch supporter, a major source of assistance and an inspiration for the achievement and development of the Nursing Archive. She was keenly aware of our need for it. The nursing profession is comparatively young — it is barely aware of the impressive history it has and is now making. The Nursing Archive gathers historically significant materials into a central place for preservation and for the use of students, scholars and researchers in nursing. It is supported by Boston University Mugar Memorial Library with assistance from a Public Health Service grant* and voluntary contributions to the Nursing Archive Fund. The publication of the Goostray Memoirs was made possible through the generosity of friends and proceeds from the sale of the book.

For those who knew and loved Stella Goostray the *Memoirs* will be quite enough to refresh their memories regarding the many activities and responsibilities in which she participated. The vita which follows may be useful to future scholars and students of nursing history.

Mary Ann L. Garrigan
Professor of Nursing
Curator, Nursing Archive
Mugar Memorial Library
Boston University
Boston, Massachusetts

*The Nursing Archive is partially supported by U.S. P.H.S. Training Grant NPG-212-03 from the Division of Nursing.

STELLA GOOSTRAY

Born in Boston, Massachusetts, July 8, 1886. Died May 8, 1969. Father —
English; mother — Scotch Canadian.

Professional Education

The Children's Hospital School of Nursing, Boston, 1919
B.S., Teachers College, Columbia University, 1926
M.Ed., Boston University, 1933

Positions Held

Instructor in Sciences, Philadelphia General Hospital School of Nursing,
1921-1922
Educational Director, Philadelphia General Hospital School of Nursing,
1922-1927
Director, School of Nursing and Nursing Service, The Children's Hospital,
Boston, 1927-1946
Adviser, Joint Committee on Educational Policies, American Nurses' Association, National League of Nursing Education, National Organization
for Public Health Nursing. January to August 1, 1930 full-time and
part-time to 1934
Part-Time Instructor, Boston University School of Nursing, 1939, 1941-
1942, 1946-1947
Part-time visitor, Accreditation Service, National League of Nursing Education, 1946-1947

Offices Held

Member, Board of Directors, 1925-1927, Secretary, 1928-1930, President,
1931-1937, American Journal of Nursing Company
Secretary, 1928-1939, President, 1940-1944, Director, 1939, 1944-1948,
National League of Nursing Education
Consultant, Committee on Grading of Nursing Schools, 1930-1934
Chairman, Subcommittee on Nursing, White House Conference on Child
Health and Protection, 1930
Member, 1930-1934, 1940-1948, Chairman, 1939-1940, Board of Registra-
tion in Nursing, Commonwealth of Massachusetts
Member, Board of Directors, 1940-1942, Nursing Council for National
Defense
President, 1942-1946, National Nursing Council for War Service, Inc.
Chairman, 1947-1950, member 1950-1953, Board of Directors, Nursing
Council of United Community Services of Boston

Member, Board of Directors, 1949-1951, and incorporator, United Community Services of Boston

Chairman, Advisory Committee, Regionalization Project in Nursing Education, Nursing Council, United Community Services of Metropolitan Boston (Newton Junior College Program in Nursing) 1956-1959

Committees

National League of Nursing Education, 1926-1952; Education, Headquarters, Studies, Curriculum, Accreditation, Administration in Schools of Nursing, Educational Problems in War Times, Post War Planning, Revision of Faculty Pamphlet, Nutting Award, Administration of Accrediting, Early Nursing Source Materials, Revision of Essentials of a Good School of Nursing

Joint Committees of American Nurses Association, National League of Nursing Education, and National Organization for Public Health Nursing, and other associations included: Cost of Nursing Services and Nursing Administration, Structure Study, Special Committee on Accrediting, Committee to work with National Association of Colored Graduate Nurses

Other Activities

Editor, *The Journal*, St. John's Episcopal Church, Roxbury Crossing, Mass., 1952-1962, Contributing Editor, 1963-1964, Vestryman, 1948-1950, 1953-1962

Past Affiliations

Regional Consultant, North Atlantic Area, Committee on Historical Source Materials in Nursing, National League for Nursing, Member of Committee 1952-1964

Member, Board of Directors, Household Nursing Association — Shepherd-Gill School of Practical Nursing, 1962-1966, Honorary Member, 1966

Committee of Consultants, Notable American Women, 1907-1950, sponsored by Radcliffe College, 1964-1969

Member, Committee on Nursing Archive, Mugar Library, Boston University, 1966-1969

Nurse Historian and Consultant, Boston University School of Nursing, 1967-1969

Member, Advisory Board Schlesinger Library, Radcliffe College, 1967-1968